SCIENCE AND THE
UNIVERSITY

SCIENCE AND THE

UNIVERSITY

EDITED BY BOYD R. KEENAN

COLUMBIA UNIVERSITY PRESS

New York and London • 1966

PREFACE

Since World War II the administering of science in the university has emerged, perhaps, as the most demanding task faced by American educators at any level. In the decades preceding the War, university administrators, as they developed their graduate schools, could find helpful organizational patterns in the great European universities. But few models have been available for handling science—especially "big science"—in the postwar years. For no country in history has provided its universities with anything to match the massive support for science that has been given American institutions of higher learning.

Most university presidents and scientists alike are among the first to admit that our institutions have, for the most part, "muddled through" these years with minimal understanding of the gigantic institutional system built by the states, the federal government, and private entities. In recent years, however, the urgency of such an understanding has been recognized. And a plethora of symposia, articles, and even books touch on problems relating to science in the university. Why, then, another book?

The great majority of such works are scattered among scholarly journals, proceedings of academic organizations, and Congressional committee hearings; satisfactory source books on the affairs of science in the university are truly rare.

This book is the outgrowth of a decision in 1964 by Purdue University's Department of Political Science to develop a special program in science and public policy. Among the department's first steps was the sponsoring, in April of 1965, of a symposium, "Science and Public Policy: Evolving Institutions." While the scope of the symposium was broader than that of the university, it seems logical— in view of the complexity of the nation's over-all institutional system— to make available in book form only those papers that deal chiefly with science and the university.

Several of the nation's most prominent scientists and administrators gave graciously of their time in pursuit of generalizations on the topic. Coming from overseas to present the keynote address and the summary presentation was Sir Eric Ashby, Master of Clare College, Cambridge, England. For the kindness and cooperation of all speakers, the Department of Political Science is deeply grateful. But perhaps an extra word of appreciation should go to Sir Eric; his presence at the program placed upon it an international aura of scholarship, charm, and academic integrity that would have been difficult to achieve without him.

Supporting funds for the symposium were provided by a National Science Foundation Institutional Grant and by the Purdue Research Foundation. The opinions contained herein are those of the individual authors, of course, and not those of the National Science Foundation, Purdue University, or the Department of Political Science.

The list of agencies and individuals responsible for the success of the symposium and the preparation of this volume is too long to enumerate. Much of the credit must go, however, to the National Science Foundation, which provided the above-mentioned grant and whose director consented to speak. Administrative officers of Purdue University also gave valuable assistance. And in addition to those authors whose works follow, several other non-Purdue scholars and public figures aided immeasurably in the planning and implementation of the symposium. Among these were Indiana Congressman Charles Halleck; Charles S. Sheldon of the National Aeronautics and Space Council staff; John Weaver, vice-president, The Ohio State University, and chairman, Committee on Institutional Cooperation; John D. Millett, chancellor-director, Ohio Board of Regents; and Jesse Hobson, vice-president, Southern Methodist University.

Faculty members of the Department of Political Science aided in the execution of the symposium and thus deserve thanks for contributing to the ultimate production of this volume. The burdens involved in transforming the symposium into a book fell chiefly upon Miss E. Frances Miller and Mrs. John A. Ritchey. And the boldness of such an undertaking by a young department would have been inconceivable had it not been for the assurance that other departmental affairs would be managed elegantly by Mrs. Patricia Johnson, departmental secretary.

Finally, the editor acknowledges with gratitude the assistance and sound counsel from the staff of the Columbia University Press in the face of obvious difficulties associated with the publication of a book with so many authors.

BOYD R. KEENAN

Lafayette, Indiana
October, 1965

CONTENTS

SCIENCE AND THE
UNIVERSITY

Boyd R. Keenan

INTRODUCTION: THE SEARCH FOR AN
INSTITUTIONAL SYSTEM FOR SCIENCE

Wherever knowledgeable men gather on the planet earth, irrespective of political ideology, two ultimate questions are asked: (1) Will mankind avoid extinction or near-extinction through successful management of a host of devices created by his own scientific genius? and (2) Will it be possible to reduce misery and suffering common to all men by transferring scientific knowledge into the practical world? These ultimate concerns are intertwined, and they have become political in nature. Failure to solve the second question is almost certain to result—sooner or later—in international holocaust that will provide a negative answer to the first.

At the top of mankind's agenda, then—and certainly the highest priority in the American dream if we are to take seriously our basic political documents—is the avoidance of world catastrophe while offering the utmost in fulfillment to the lone individual, be he a resident of Peoria, Illinois, or Djakarta, Indonesia. But while the single individual remains the sacred unit in our preferred political system, the time is now past when one man or even a small band of men can attack either the "catastrophe" item or the "fulfillment" item.

Weapons systems, medical science research teams, and scientists involved in space exploration are all managed by gigantic institutions.[1] Most are either governmental agencies or nongovernmental

---

[1] A great deal of controversy exists among social scientists over a definition of the word "institution." While it is hoped that much of this controversy may be bypassed in this volume, the use of the terms "institution" and "organization" necessitates classification.

For a superb analysis of the conflicting usages both of "institution" and

organizations responsible indirectly to political decision-makers. All such scientific operations utilize the talents of hundreds—even thousands—of skilled individuals. From cancer research to the investigation of the nature of matter itself through giant accelerators, the picture is the same: The needs of science have become so great for our society—yea, for all societies—that science has indeed become institutionalized.[2] And it must become even more institutionalized if the "catastrophe" and "fulfillment" agenda items are to be handled successfully. But systematic attempts to understand the burgeoning institutions of science have been rare. So overwhelming is the task that few practitioners or scholars have given the agonizing attention needed to draw parameters around the broad system and define the complex elements or subsystems within it.

There is no escaping the fact that scientific institutions—operated by governments—already control the destiny of mankind. Shrinkage of the world through improved communications, especially in the scientific areas, requires that any meaningful description of the institutional system encompass all nations. A scientific institution yet unbuilt in a nation yet unrecognized for such talents may produce the knowledge leading to conquests over cancer or an anti-weapons system making obsolete the most gigantic bomb that at present exists.

The long-range search for a comprehensive scientific institutional system must, then, be an international one. However, only Sir Eric Ashby's first paper covers types of scientific institutions existing

---

"organization" see Amitai Etzioni, *Modern Organizations* (Englewood Cliffs, N.J., Prentice Hall, 1964), p. 3. The author agrees with Etzioni's claim that the term "institution" might well be discarded entirely in favor of the simple term "organization" as a label for all planned units, deliberately structured for the purpose of attaining specific goals. However, in view of the nature of this volume—which has drawn upon specialists from a variety of disciplines—an attempt is made in this paper to retain a dichotomy in the relationship of the two concepts. While admittedly artificial and perhaps outmoded, the option of retaining the dichotomy seems a wiser one than that of spending several paragraphs—if not pages—resisting the more popular dichotomous handling of the concept. See Philip Selznick, *Leadership in Administration* (Evanston, Ill., Row, Peterson and Co., 1957), for definitions generally followed in this paper. For Selznick, an organization is expendable—merely a means to an end—while an institution is not expendable. It develops deeper loyalties and attachments.

[2] Selznick, p. 17, contends that "to institutionalize is to infuse with value, which means developing something more basic than mere technique."

across the world. While the question is a universal one, it seems logical to begin the search in a familiar arena. Thus, with the exception just noted, the essays that follow center on the American scientific institutional system and the role of the university within this broad system. This provincialism, we believe, is less serious than it may first appear. The success of the United States in gearing itself organizationally for the production of the atomic bomb near the end of World War II and its spectacular pursuit of the Soviet Union in the field of space science following the launching of Sputnik in 1957 together have called attention to the nation's ability to institutionalize science and technology in time of crisis. Similarly, the readiness of many nations, both advanced and lesser developed, to adapt American models in their own scientific institutions suggests that an emphasis upon the institutional system in the United States will not be without comparative implications.

THE NEW POLITICS OF SCIENTIFIC INSTITUTIONS

The search for a scientific institutional system is no less political than it is international. Powerful sovereign political units must make ultimate decisions based on knowledge assembled by institutions. In the United States, at least, today's multifarious scientific organizations grew out of a post–World War II era in which not even the most visionary of our government officials could anticipate the significance of the nation's scientific establishment twenty years hence. These papers indeed indicate that we have reached critical crossroads in the development of scientific institutions. That the question is a political one, then, no one can deny. The eloquence of the spokesmen for the various types of scientific organizations in America persuades us that we have—almost unnoticed—moved into a period that might be called the era of the politics of institutional rivalry. Certainly included in this new scientific system are the well-publicized competitive relationships among the various federal agencies and the competition among states and regions for the federal research dollar.

Not so well publicized, however, but perhaps even more significant for the American political system, is the rivalry among profit-making corporations and relatively new nonprofit independent organizations that are in competition with each other as well as with the "in-house" federal laboratory, the university, and the federal contract center operated by either an industrial corporation or a university. To label this area of study the "politics of scientific institutions" does not, of course, reflect adversely on the proponents of the various types of scientific institutions. Quite the contrary—in the sense the word is used here—"politics" is the stuff that advances civilization. And answers to the "catastrophe" and "fulfillment" questions raised above must come from the political arena. It is to the credit of the spokesmen for these scientific organizations that they have confidence that their brands of institution—or the type that they propose for the future— will best answer our needs.

THE INSTITUTIONAL SYSTEM AND ITS SUBSYSTEMS

A new intellectual task—world-wide in nature—faces those who would guide mankind's future development. *It is the construction of an institutional system for science.* The American scientific edifice is a monument to many dedicated scientists and public servants. But none can deny that it is also the product of a multiplicity of unconnected crash programs, haphazard coordination, and plain political accidents. The plea here is not for a centralized, decentralized, or any other particular institutional pattern but for conceptualization of the system that does now exist. Forgetting, for the moment, the organizations and institutions of science in other nations, how can one simplify the range of existing scientific institutions in the United States?

The interlocking of public agencies with private organizations prevents a firm differentiation along these lines, yet one has nowhere else to begin but with these categories. As in the case of many large, private universities, it may be that an institution is supported in great measure by a formal governmental agency, but nevertheless for purposes of analysis we must distinguish between those units operating actually as governmental institutions and those that have only a contractual or similar relationship with government. At the level of the federal government the formal scientific units are most often described as "intramural performers" while nongovernmental organizations receive the label "extramural performers." Granted that these definitions become artificial at times, they may, in fact, become even more necessary in usage as state, municipal, and even formal interstate governmental units develop their own scientific organizations or arrange new quasi-governmental innovations to handle scientific matters.

To oversimplify, then, the scientific institutions in the United States are either operated directly by a governmental unit or by a nongovernmental organization. Illustrative of the difficulty arising from this oversimplification is the existence of federal contract research centers that are actually governmental laboratories operated by either profit-making organizations or by nonprofit institutions such as universities. The major point here is that the scientific institutional system is made up of complex subsystems and that little has yet been done to describe these elements and develop a synthesis of the relationship of these various elements to our political process.

Few of these subsystems have been scrutinized against the backdrop of our political ideologies. The controversial questions relating to patents when inventions are produced by private corporations through public funds are among the most visible dilemmas, but the vast labyrinthine system of scientific institutions holds equally perplexing problems. And, as always, solutions must rest upon understanding. In turn, understanding rests upon the construction of a broad system that encompasses the profit-making organizations, universities, and a host of other nonprofit institutions which exercise some but not all of the functions traditionally allotted to the university in this country.

THE VULNERABILITY OF THE UNIVERSITY AS A SUBSYSTEM

Belief that the construction of such an institutional system for science is critical to the national interest led, then, to a symposium on the topic "Science and Public Policy: Evolving Institutions." At this symposium, which was held on April 12–14, 1965, at Purdue University and was sponsored by its Department of Political Science, the papers appearing in this volume were presented. The conference was planned well in advance of widely publicized "student alienation" episodes at the Berkeley campus of the University of California and at other universities throughout the nation. And, frankly, the agenda included no section on the plight of the student at the scientific institution. But it became apparent from the formal papers presented and

ensuing discussions that the scientific character of the American
university could not be neatly considered aside from the complex
problems so often decried presently under this rubric of "student
alienation." Indeed, a symposium structured months before the
Berkeley crisis and with little regard for the relationship of student
problems to research became a forum where this issue received an
airing by many of the nation's most influential scientific administrators and educators. It seemed, then, that the university was the institution most seriously charged with failing to perform its societal functions. No doubt the timing of the Berkeley riots contributed to the
prevalence of these challenges. But it seems likely that the embarrass-
ing questions aimed at representatives of some of America's greatest
universities were not triggered but merely reinforced by the concurrent activities at Berkeley. Those of us with university responsibilities became increasingly uncomfortable as the symposium progressed.
Several top-level scientific administrators from the federal government strongly questioned some assumptions that have almost sacred
status on university campuses. Perhaps even more disquieting to the
university scientists—social as well as natural—were the expressions
of approval voiced by graduate students and young instructors after
hearing challenges hurled at the universities by a new breed of executive, the independent research administrator. Equally disconcerting to
the university representatives were the almost awesome predictions of
the future independent research organizations that this new breed will
manage and that are already competing with the universities for research funds.

This does not mean, of course, that university spokesmen failed in
an attempt to defend their institutions. But any objective summary of
the symposium could not ignore a new kind of political rivalry between the university and the newly emerging institutions in the scientific community. Some defenders of the university would contend
that the university bore the major brunt of the criticism as a result of
its position as the oldest type of scientific institution under consideration. And nearly all university administrators present gave vent to the
frustrations that face them at the present time as they seek to provide
identifiable directions in diverse areas such as teaching, research, and
service.

Cropping up in any discussion of this topic are such phrases as "the dehumanization of college teaching." At Berkeley and elsewhere teaching is said by many to have suffered because of emphasis on research. And yet if one accepts the basic assumptions drawn earlier in this paper, nearly all human fulfillment and survival depend upon research. The coupling of the student alienation episodes with the obvious societal needs for even more research does indeed leave the university vulnerable. Suggestions that the university reinforce its teaching function while leaving more of the research function to newly emerging independent research organizations, both profit and nonprofit, were heard at the symposium and are increasingly being heard elsewhere.

The universities remain uncertain because those of us on campuses have not adequately answered the critics in regard to the university's future role in this scientific institutional system. A partial answer is that a sizable portion of our nation's research, both basic and applied, must remain in the universities to aid in our instructional responsibilities, if for no other reason. Yet we must admit that emphasis on research has critically changed the character of the universities and that student alienation is only one of many curses that will plague us if we are not successful in constructing a more logical university subsystem within the broad scientific institutional system. If any university participants in the symposium harbored the hope that the university would yet be allowed to work out its problems independently, they likely left the meeting disabused of this notion. Spokesmen for federal laboratories and independent research organizations serve notice in the following papers that they view the crises of the university—or the "multiversity," as it is so often called in these days—as their business, too.

THE FUTURE OF MULTIPURPOSE INSTITUTIONS

Papers delivered at the symposium and concurrent happenings across the nation made it clear that the university will be fair game from now on as the knowledge industry is increasingly recognized as holding the growth stock of our century.

From one side of the aisle came statements from representatives of the nonteaching institutions that the real purpose of the university is education and it jolly well better get back at the job and leave "big science" to independent research organizations. The time has come —the argument seemed to run—to realize that our critical problems just will not permit the university to continue as the powerful multipurpose organization.

Indeed it is true that the university is a multipurpose organization simultaneously serving at least two goals. There are probably more universities operating today that combine teaching with research than there are organizations that are primarily devoted to teaching (most colleges) or organizations that are devoted solely to research. In the latter category would be such organizations as the Battelle Memorial Institute, the RAND Corporation, and the Stanford Research Institute. Spokesmen for many such independent research institutes conscientiously believe that many critical goals associated with big science are simply incompatible with the educational goals to which universities must aspire.

The right of the university to continue at its present level as a multipurpose institution was also challenged by Alvin Weinberg, director of the Oak Ridge National Laboratory. In effect, he charged that the traditional attention to basic research on university campuses has dulled the taste for action and that action—critically needed action—is not likely to come from professors who devalue the useful. Weinberg admitted that his perspective was that of a vice-president of a private profit-making organization, Union Carbide Corporation, which operates the Oak Ridge National Laboratory as a federal contract research center for the Atomic Energy Commission. And Weinberg, like spokesmen for the independent research organizations, appeared to be basing his concern on the multipurpose character of the university.

Much of the discomfort among the academicians was heightened by recent rumors that many large corporations are entering the knowledge industry through "Great Society" contracts in an effort to explore the real possibilities of biting off chunks of the industry that might result in handsome profits in the decades ahead. It seemed to some educators that they were witnesses to prescriptions of the decline of the university as a multipurpose institution while at the same time being given a preview of the blooming of nonuniversity organizations into this very sort of enterprise.

One of the university's own, Edward Teller, joined the parade of dissenters who felt that the university is not adequately pursuing action-oriented programs or rewarding those scholars who might make sacrifices to apply their knowledge to practical matters. One route to a remedy for the lack of applied scientists, Teller suggested, would be to allow nonuniversity organizations to grant respectable PH.D. degrees to bright students who wish to become modern inventors. Such a step would, of course, serve to create a new type of multipurpose institution.

It is clear that efforts are moving simultaneously to reduce the influence of some of our greatest scientific institutions and to build yet other such establishments. From the papers that follow it is also clear that men of good spirit and integrity are involved in these two processes of institution-debilitation and institution-building. What is not so obvious is that the processes are well understood. But it is likely that holders of the purse strings at both federal and state levels will likely demand proof in the decades ahead that fund recipients—university scientists and others—are striving to relate all efforts to a grand and practical system. Failure of professors and university administrators to recognize concern among responsible politicians could very well result in an emasculation of great research universities. This will occur if the university fails to hammer out new goals in a rapidly changing world. All institutions are conservative, but the academic rank structure, accompanying tenure arrangements, and difficulty in measuring academic achievement all compound the problems of inertia in a university.

Profit measurement and other devices are open to most nonuniversity organizations to prevent empire building that is not in keeping with the character of the institution as envisaged by the responsible leaders. The existing project system of grants and contracts utilized by the government contributes to the difficulty of university administrators who attempt to identify unique thrusts that their institutions may make. Frederick Seitz, president of the National Academy of Sciences, devotes much of his paper to this subject. Comments by a lesser figure in the scientific establishment could, perhaps, be taken lightly. But his unabashed warning of the consequences of further proliferation of federal grants directly to professors without regard to the total character of the university underlines the seriousness of the situation. As more and more academic disciplines, including the social sciences, extend their own lines to agencies in Washington, the problem is intensified. It is clear that many scientist-statesmen with Washington experience feel the need for stronger leadership from presidents, deans, and department heads in order that institutional directions can be chartered relative to the federal government's resources.

Disregarding any value consideration, it seems inevitable that nonuniversity organizations will increasingly attempt to perform certain of the functions that have traditionally remained within the university's domain. And it is far from clear what type of institution would emerge to fill the vacuum should the university fail to meet this all-important challenge of defining and adhering to new goals.

CROSSROADS TO WHERE?

Of the emerging subsystems within the American scientific institutional system, the nonprofit varieties receive the bulk of the attention in the following papers. This is especially noticeable—and perhaps surprising—when one realizes that probably more than 60 percent of federal research and development is being handled by the great profit-making corporations of America. The lack of attention given to private corporations engaged in scientific activities does not, of course, reflect any judgment that their contributions are less significant or that their piece of the research pie should be reduced. Rather it reflects the belief of the symposium planners that the private profit-making sector—as major components in the system under study—has elsewhere been more adequately analyzed than the elements covered here in such detail. The greatest gap in the literature of our scientific institutional system, it is hoped, will be narrowed by the emphasis on the innovative organizational forms little understood beyond the boundaries of their own subsystems. Many spokesmen for these subsystems believe that the American scientific enterprise, and its institutions, stands at the crossroads. If it is indeed true that our nation's house of scientific intellect now controls not only our chances for preserving our political freedoms but our physical survival as well, the urgency of the question need not be stressed further. The nation's grand scientific institutional system must at least be understood, and the converging institutional routes must be programmed for all eventualities. Until this is accomplished neither the scientist nor the political leader can stand, at least figuratively, at these crossroads and debate alternative paths for the future. The seriousness of decisions to be made requires us to scrutinize all existing types of institutions as well as the models yet on the drawing boards. We have observed that no institution—not even the university—will be sancrosanct in the agonizing examinations that must continue in the years before us.

Much as the scientists have been honored, even worshipped, it is now apparent that politicians will make the critical decisions regarding the future of scientific institutions. Just as the day of the single scientist working alone in his laboratory is behind us, so is the era when scientists themselves can tell the politicians how to build a national scientific establishment. Now that the critical relationship between scientific institutions and survival is recognized by all intelligent men, the cry to keep politics out of science is as unrealistic as an aim to keep sex out of courtship and marriage.

But where are we going institutionally? We shall go where political forces take us. A few decades ago there was widespread hope that self-contained within the biological evolutionary process was the continuous moral improvement of man. But the dogmas of Nazism, Stalinism, and Imperialism—all produced by political forces—proved this hope to be ill founded. And now with this knowledge and the awareness that scientific advances have brought us to the brink of total annihilation as well as to the threshold of unbelievable possibilities for individual fulfillment, we seek inspiration to fashion institutions capable of facing the challenge.

The phrase "political forces" has an ominous air. And it will likely be a prophetic air if we succumb to the vertiginous feeling that the Marxists have made the foundation of their philosophy. This is the notion that the real control of life has passed from men to the "things," to the "laws," to something called "history." But the sense of loss of control of one's own destiny is not limited to the Marxists. Our own passionate intentness on the instruments of life, invented and manu-factured in our scientific institutions, could lead us by a different route to the same abyss.

While serious in nature, the papers that follow do not emit such a tone. Rather they emphasize the sense of wonder in Nature, a free-dom within her boundaries, and of unity with her in knowledge. Such knowledge is, we know, available in our scientific institutions, and, if we successfully manage them, it is possible that our children's children—perhaps even our children—will experience a depth of joy in life yet unimagined by even the most wise among us.

Sir Eric Ashby

SCIENCE AND PUBLIC POLICY: SOME INSTITUTIONAL PATTERNS OUTSIDE AMERICA

"Science and Public Policy: Some Institutional Patterns" is a high-sounding title. Let us begin by deflating it. The purpose of scientific institutions is to promote science. They have no other end in themselves. Therefore the subject under consideration is the piecrust, not the pie. Nevertheless, let us not underrate the piecrust. Science can no longer be done outside institutions; without piecrusts there would be no pies.

An institution for the promotion of science must perform one or other of three functions: it must be a place where science is advanced, or communicated, or applied. Let us note straight away a peculiarity of all such institutions. It is this: the advancement, the communication, and the application of science cannot be done by presidents, or boards of trustees, or administrators, or committees, or legislatures, or financiers; it can be done only by scientists. Herein lies the central problem of science and public policy. Initiative for the promotion of science must come from the level of the scientist, from the laboratory bench; yet the power to create, maintain, and finance scientific institutions is nowadays beyond the capacity of scientists: it must be done by the public, the foundations, and industry—the patrons of science.

The problem is an ethical one. For the scientist the problem is how much freedom he should demand from the patron who hires him; for the patron it is how much freedom should be given to the scientist he has hired. In this context it simply is not true to say that the man who pays the piper calls the tune. What happens in fact is that in every scientific institution an equilibrium is established between patron and scientist. But the exact point of equilibrium depends not only on patrons and scientists; it depends also on the function of the institution (whether it is a university or a research institute or an industrial laboratory); and it depends on the national social climate—whether it is a *laissez-faire* society or a totalitarian state. It must depend, too, upon the interests of the region or community which supports the institution. Public policy touches science at three points: first, and certainly most important, over the training of scientists; second, over the control of scientific institutions; third, over the support of specific projects. Discussions of public policy for science tend to become dangerously exothermic. For example, Michael Polanyi condemns indignantly any effort to plan scientific strategy. "Any attempt," he says, "at guiding scientific research toward a purpose other than its own is to deflect it from the advancement of science." To give another example, Alvin Weinberg believes that the decision whether or not to embark on expensive research projects should be made on "external" criteria, namely the technological, scientific, and social merits of the project.

In this paper I shall say something about patterns of equilibrium outside the United States. I am faced with two alternatives: either I must select two or three examples and risk criticism by recklessly generalizing from them, or I must bore the reader with details. I have chosen the first alternative.

First I shall speak of Britain. Let us cut out straight away some 65 percent of Britain's total expenditure on research and development, for this either is inside industry or is on defense in government establishments, and it is not narrowly relevant to the discussion. This leaves some 35 percent of expenditure (of the order of $500 million) on civilian research in four kinds of institutions, namely, (*a*) government departments and government research councils; (*b*) universities and colleges of technology; (*c*) research associations which are cooperative enterprises, financed partly by government and partly by contributions from industry, to serve dispersed industries such as ceramics, flour millers, and leather manufacturers; and (*d*) public corporations, such as the General Post Office. Two of these categories are enough to illustrate my theme: (1) universities and colleges of technology and (2) the research councils.

There are no private universities or colleges of technology in Britain. They are all financed from public funds. I would make a rough-and-ready guess that 88 cents of every dollar of the income of British universities is public money. Yet the British universities behave as autonomous corporations. Nearly all the recurrent income they receive from the state is "free" money, not earmarked for particular purposes. And they give no account of their expenditure to Parliament. Far from calling the tune, the man who pays the piper never even hears the tune—officially at any rate.

The mechanism that so effectively insulates British universities from the cross winds of politics is the University Grants Committee (UGC). For five years I have served on this committee, so I can describe it to you from the inside. Technically it is a committee of the Ministry of Education and Science. It has a permanent salaried chairman (an ex-university president) and a part-time deputy chairman, but its eighteen members are neither civil servants nor politicians, but private citizens who give their services; thirteen of them are academics (professors or heads of colleges), three are drawn from industry, and two are drawn from the rest of the education system.

The fascinating feature of the committee's work does not appear on paper at all: it lies in the conventions that have been built up over its administration of grants. For years there has been a dialectic between the Public Accounts Committee, which is the financial watchdog of the legislature, and the UGC. The Public Accounts Committee, not unreasonably, wants some account given to Parliament of the way money is spent by universities. The UGC asserts that accountability to Parliament would be bound to lead sooner or later to infringement of the autonomy of universities. Every now and again the discussion comes to the surface; and so far the Press and public opinion support the universities. The convention of nonaccountability runs through the whole system. At the top, the UGC does not disclose either to government or to universities the principles on which it distributes public money; at the bottom, it does not require the universities to justify their recurrent expenditure of public money as between, say, arts faculties and science faculties or agriculture and engineering.

Insofar as research is regarded as an integral part of a university teacher's job and laboratories and libraries are used for research, a notional percentage of the UGC grant to universities can be attributed to research. The estimate is that the British universities are spending this year about $104 million of their own (state-derived) income on research, most of it in science and technology. But there is another very important source of income: it is the policy in Britain to finance special needs in university research from what are called the research councils. These are now in process of being rearranged by the Labour Government, but it will illustrate my theme best if I describe how they have functioned in the recent past.

There are four of them: the Agricultural Research Council; the Nature Conservancy; the Medical Research Council; and the Council for Scientific and Industrial Research. They have three main activities. First, they control research institutes of their own with a scientific staff of 10,000. These people work on research projects that in theory are approved from above each year by the councils but in practice are due primarily to the initiative of the scientific staff itself. Second, they have established in universities a number of research units (there were about 100 of these in 1963–64) that use the laboratories of the university and that include staff who may do some teaching and who certainly play an essential part in training research workers. The research units work on long-range problems that the councils think worthy of support. The dramatic advances in molecular biology achieved by British scientists have been made in an MRC unit attached to Cambridge University. Third, they make grants to individuals in universities to carry out research. Without these grants scientific research in British universities would be crippled, for we have nothing like the resources of private foundations that America has. The keynote of these grants is that they are given not to projects or departments but to individual people. In the British self-governing universities there is always a very strong element of egalitarianism. Two departments with equal numbers of students consider that they should have budgets of equal size, even though one department may be bursting with enterprise and activity and the other may be as stagnant as a Spanish convent. So it is an essential part of public policy in Britain that university research should be financed mainly through the four research councils. They

do this in two ways; one, by giving three-year maintenance grants
£425 per annum) to thousands of students working for PH.D.s (any
one who gets a good honors degree in science and technology can
now get a maintenance grant to work for a PH.D.); and the other,
by giving grants for technical assistance and expensive equipment to
individual scientific workers. These grants in 1963–64 amounted to
about $37 million (this included $21 million as grants to individual
workers and $10 million to support postgraduate studentships). This
constitutes between one fourth and one third of the whole expenditure on research by universities. So, to sum up, when you cut
out defense expenditure on research, nine tenths of which is done
in government departments, and expenditure on research and development in private industry, nine tenths of which is done by industry itself, you find that about a fifth of all government-supported
research is done in universities and is financed primarily through two
channels: the four research councils and the UGC. Industry contributes only about a fiftieth. A little comes from the foundations.
There are very few research contracts of the kind familiar to Americans, though we in the United Kingdom receive considerable sums
from United States contracts.

Finally, I come to the principal point about the research councils.
They, like the UGC, are run by academics, not by politicians or civil
servants. The Council for Scientific and Industrial Research (on
which I served for five years) consisted of six academic scientists and
technologists appointed after consultation with the Royal Society,
two industrialists, and a representative of the trade unions. The Agricultural Research Council and Medical Research Council are similarly composed of working scientists drawn predominantly from the
universities and invited after consultation with the Royal Society.

One last feature of the organization of British science: it remains
very flexible and without much cohesion because it is still true that
most of the distinguished scientists are still in universities, not in industry or in scientific establishments of the government. Three
fourths of the present Fellows of the Royal Society, for instance,
work in universities, and our universities are still essentially self-
governing academic societies.

Now I shall mention briefly two patterns of science and public policy that contrast with the pattern that we have evolved in Britain and exported with some success to various parts of the Commonwealth. I have selected two of which I have some knowledge at firsthand: Germany and the USSR.

Germany is the home of a mystique of higher education that still determines public policy. The first element of this mystique is that any student who has completed a high-school course in a *Gymnasium* and has his qualification, called *Abitur,* has a right to enroll at a university. The expansion of facilities has not been consistent with this principle, so classrooms are scandalously overcrowded. But the *Lernfreiheit* that allows any qualified young German to study where and what he likes has been preserved. The drop-out rate is high. Unlike the British policy, which selects rigorously those who shall be admitted to universities and regards drop-out as a sign of inefficient selection, the German policy is to allow any student to enter and to eliminate the weak ones during their undergraduate career.

A second element of the mystique is that the university is regarded primarily as a research institute. The professor in his laboratory, surrounded by a few picked disciples, is still the ideal of German academic life. Accordingly, it is still accepted as a basic article of faith that teaching is inseparable from research in German universities—indeed, in case of a conflict, teaching gives way to research—and every candidate for the *Diplome* has to do a piece of research. Any drift in policy that separates research from teaching in German universities would be bitterly resisted.

Universities in Germany are the responsibility of the states (Länder). They are financed from public funds by the Länder. The professors are state civil servants; appointments are made by the Minister. Therefore, like Australia and America, Germany has to reconcile a strongly built-in pluralism in its institutions of higher education with the need for some central coordination of policy for science and technology. This reconciliation is effected through three channels, which I shall now describe to you.

The first is the German Research Council (Deutsche Forschungsgemeinschaft, known as DFG). The DFG has no institutes of its own. It receives funds from the federal and state governments. It uses these, as the research councils do in Britain, to finance individual men and projects in universities. Some of its income comes from an association of industrialists (the Stifterverband) that makes voluntary donations to promote research. The aim of the Stifterverband is that every industry shall give 1 percent of its annual dividend or profits to the Stifterverband for distribution—without earmarking—to research institutes in universities and outside them. The DFG is run by a senate of twenty-seven members, most of them elected by the universities; so this is another example of the solution reached in Britain, namely, that the controllers are drawn from the controlled. (There is also a board of trustees, which includes representatives of the contributing governments.) A scientific institute in a university reckons on getting its salaries and its "bread-and-butter" supplies from the university grant; but its research grants come from the DFG or from certain big industries (Volkswagen, for instance).

Beside the DFG there is another body which helps to crystallize public policy: the Council for Arts and Science (Wissenschaftsrat). This was set up by an agreement between federal and state governments in 1957 to coordinate higher education and research in West Germany. It reports to the President of the Republic. It has no executive authority, but its recommendations, which must be unanimous, carry great weight. Already it has produced several reports, including a 500-page document on the development of institutions of higher education.

In addition, there is a remarkable institution, the Max Planck Gesellschaft zur Förderung der Wissenschaften, which is the chief institution for scientific research in Germany. It was founded in 1911 as the Kaiser Wilhelm Gesellschaft. Its purpose was to provide privately financed institutes to enable distinguished scientists to pursue research outside the civil service (which includes the universities), with no obligation to work according to any plan imposed from above, and undeterred by the duties associated with posts in the universities and polytechnic institutes. The project was immensely successful. At the end of World War I there were twenty institutes, and the workers included Einstein, Emil Fischer, Otto Warburg, Otto Hahn, and Heisenberg. In 1948 the institutes were reorganized as Max Planck Gesellschaft. Today there are forty-five of them; they range from genetics and neurology to astrophysics and metallurgy.

Each institute is virtually autonomous; once it has received its finances from the central administration, its director is the sole arbiter of what goes on in his laboratory. The idea that the institutes could be financed privately was long ago abandoned. The present pattern of finance is roughly 10 percent from private sources, 45 percent from the Länder (corresponding to the states in the United States), and 45 percent from the federal government. But there seems to be no anxiety about interference from those who distribute public funds. There is a board of directors, which includes men from public life and industry, and a scientific board, which includes the directors of institutes. Like the UGC and the research councils in Britain, these act as baffle plates between the scientist and the politician. The autonomy of the Max Planck Gesellschaft is a matter of great pride.

Of course, autonomy is difficult to reconcile with planning, and one does not hear in Germany a great deal about coordination and planning of science. I have the impression that, unless massive finance is involved—in which case the federal government and the Länder would be obliged to consult and coordinate their activities—there is a tolerance of pluralism in scientific effort and a belief that competition among scientists in different institutions (for example, Max Planck laboratories and universities) is healthy and worth encouraging.

My third example is from the USSR. Here, at first sight, public policy is poles apart from the policy pursued in Western countries. The equilibrium between scientist and patron lies heavily on the side of the patron. Over higher education, for instance, there is a fundamentally different philosophy. I suppose it could be said that the size and pattern of the American system of higher education is determined by the pressure of candidates wanting to get into it; a bachelor's degree is consumer goods. The size and pattern of the Soviet system is determined by the suction at the graduate end: the state's needs for manpower. Standards of entry, curricula, standards of graduation, scholarships to meet the cost of college—all these are centrally controlled, and the control is used to manipulate the flow of trained manpower. All higher education is professional training.

The resulting pattern is, I am sure, familiar to you, for the best summaries in English have been made by Americans. There are over seven hundred institutions of higher education in the USSR; only forty of them are universities, and the universities contain only 10 percent of the total student population. A boy who wants to be a doctor goes to a medical school under the Ministry of Health; a boy who wants to be a mechanical engineer goes to a college under the Ministry to Heavy Industry, and so on. Enrollment into these institutes is controlled by adjusting entrance standards and numbers of scholarships. The universities produce almost exclusively scholars, research workers, and teachers. Other kinds of professionals get their training outside universities. The origin of this pattern is Napoleon's France, where the highest professional training was in the *grandes écoles,* not in the universities. But the Russians have introduced two important features that reflect public policy about the training of scientists: one is that in all higher education, however vocational its purpose, is included a sizable ingredient of humanities. For example, a student reading for a diploma in automation at the Institute of Power Engineering may spend up to 15 percent of his time on nontechnical subjects, including a compulsory foreign language. The other feature is a much greater degree of specialization for the proposed job in the last two years of the five-year course. Thus a man does not major in physics: he majors in solid state physics or particle physics or electronic physics, and so on.

So much for the training of scientists. Of greater relevance to our subject is the organization of scientific research. The seat of nearly all research in pure science is the Academy of Sciences (we have to remember that the Russian word *nauk,* like the German *Wissenschaft,* stands for much more than science in our sense: it stands for all scholarship). The Academy has some 160 institutes (largely concentrated in Moscow and Leningrad) with a staff of some 17,000, including over 500 members of the Academy—a status symbol as sought after as membership of the National Academy in America or Fellowship of the Royal Society in Britain! But even the Academy is subject to planning. Recent events in the Soviet Union provide an instructive lesson in the way public policy is brought to bear upon science.

In a speech at the Plenum of the Central Committee of the Communist Party in June, 1959, Khrushchev called for a reform of the Academy of Sciences. Promptly, according to traditional Soviet procedure, Academician Semenov published in August an article in *Izvestiia* with proposals for overhauling the whole structure of the Academy. In particular, he said that the technological institutes should be removed from the Academy and put under Gosplan. This caused a great stir and gave rise to one of those public controversies in the daily press which, in the USSR, one suspects are entirely artificial and contrived. A few days later, in *Izvestiia,* Academician Bardin, a metallurgist, crossed swords with Academician Semenov. Bardin maintained that technology should be kept within the Academy, for science and technology are inseparable. What was wrong with the Academy, said Bardin, was its bureaucracy, which "turns research workers into office managers." Other Academicians joined in, each with his particular solution and his particular criticism of the Academy. These heart-searchings continued until the annual meeting of the Academy in February, 1960, when the President, Academician Nesmeyanov, propounded what was evidently the temporary Party line, but with no clear-cut solution. The Academy was evidently still under political pressure, and one guesses that the eminent Academicians were resisting the pressure. It was not until a year later, when the Council of Ministers had evidently made a major political decision about the organization of science, that the august Academy found itself subjected to a scientific planning authority above itself.

Universities in the USSR are not—as in America or Britain or Germany—distinguished centers for research. The Russian professor is ambivalent in his attitude toward this. On one hand, any research he cares to do is not being planned from above, so he has a freedom to follow his own inclinations, and, if he is on a line of work that does not need expensive equipment, he can carry on quietly on his own, undisturbed by the feverish attempts to fit scientific programs into a national scheme that goes on in research institutes. So some professors welcome the fact that they are not expected to be very productive. On the other hand, he does not have the opportunities of his colleagues in the institutes of the Academy, and, therefore, he cannot hold his own in his profession. Some scientists get the best of both worlds by having a plurality of posts (a chair in a university and a post in some Academy institute); and the Academy institutes now cooperate with universities on a large scale in the training of research workers. Recently, too, there has been an attempt to inject more research into universities by founding some three hundred "problems laboratories" subsidized to carry out special research projects. They are somewhat similar to the units that British research councils plant in our universities.

As I stated above, the seat of nearly all research in pure science is in the Academy. But the total volume of applied research and development in the USSR is so enormous that the Academy's program forms only a small fraction of the total effort: it takes up only 8 percent of the country's scientific budget and employs only 6.5 percent of the country's scientific staff. It is a central mystique of Soviet society that all this immense effort should be planned and coordinated. When one recollects that every one of the fifteen "autonomous" republics of the Soviet Union has its own Academy and universities and industrial research institutes, one begins to grasp the difficulties of living with this mystique. However, there is a constant stream of propaganda for the more efficient planning of science, and scientists cannot disregard this.

For many years all planning in Soviet education and science has had to be consistent with the central Gosplan. Even twenty years ago, when I was living in Russia as a diplomatist, each scientific institute had to "fulfill its plan," and this gave rise to many ironical jokes. I remember how one distinguished biochemist (now dead) kept on the right side of the planners. "During the first year's work of my institute," he said, "we got a lot of work done; but I persuaded the authorities that we were still setting up the laboratories and had nothing to report; then I used for my plan for my second year what was really my report on the first year; and I have kept that up ever since. We know before the year starts that we shall fulfill the plan, for we have already fulfilled it."

It is instructive, therefore, to find, twenty years later, that the belief that science can be planned still survives. The latest improvement in the planning machinery since 1961 is the creation of a Committee for the Coordination of Scientific Research. This committee has no executive functions but gigantic power, for it controls all key scientific research and it has to approve all major projects in science and technology. Its chairman is a deputy prime minister; its membership includes the President of the Academy of Sciences—the Academy is as subject to its decisions as any other institution—and the Minister for Higher Education. The committee has already set up thirty scientific councils; it has 5,000 scientists on its panels of advisers; it has a staff of 400, many of them experts who spend their time scrutinizing research programs. Among other recent changes to improve the planning of science are the publication by the Academy of a fascinating list called the "thirty basic directions of science," which sets out the fields to which high priority is to be given, and the removal from the Academy of most of the institutes dealing with technology—they are now under the appropriate industrial ministries, though still coordinated by the new master committee.

The Soviet Union has a massive hierarchical framework for the planning of science to meet the needs of Soviet society. Since every citizen in the Soviet Union is a servant of the state—even ballet dancers and novelists—it is possible through this framework to divert great masses of skilled men and money from one project to another, with results (in space-technology, for instance) that are very impressive. But let us not forget that in the interstices of this framework there is plenty of room for initiative. Soviet scientists have learned how to tame these monsters of planning. In conversation they agree that planning must come from below upward, and it is understood that, provided 60–80 percent of the effort of an institute is consistent with the over-all national plan, the balance of effort can be used as individual scientists think best. And there is still, I believe, room for some pluralism in the source of funds; through suitable lobbying a proposal that is turned down by one ministry may be encouraged by another. The merit of the Soviet system in my mind is the very easy transition from laboratory experiment to pilot-scale tryout. That is something we lack in Britain.

Let us return to the British pattern.

For scientific research in Britain we still have a government-sponsored *laissez-faire* economy. Policy for spending public money is put into the hands of representatives of the pipers, not of those who pay the pipers. The philosophical assumption made by the pipers is that nonintervention produces the best results. If you invest in good men and good departments and leave the initiative to them, you will get the best return. Accordingly, there is a minimum of direction from above and a contrived pluralism for the sources of finance for research. I believe this policy has bad as well as good consequences. The good ones are evident. For a university or an individual to be given an un-earmarked grant or salary and to be told, "Do the work you want to do: we trust you," is the sort of challenge a good man responds to, and it is producing original scientific work of the highest quality. But there are drawbacks. For one thing, there is not the sensitive response to national needs that a more hierarchical system produces, and this sometimes means that the applications of science to society (which do not interest many scientists) are neglected. In addition, the entrustment of policy-forming to working scientists does assume that policy-forming is a sort of hobby to be done in a scientist's spare time. Many scientists have the experience of serving on scientific policy committees. They receive, as I do, a packet of agenda papers weighing perhaps half a kilogram. They may, as I sometimes do, run over them during the weekend, but one does not really concentrate one's mind on the agenda until one is in the train or plane going to the meeting. (The railroad service from Cambridge to London is notoriously slow; but this is a blessing in disguise, for it gives those of us from Cambridge time to study the agenda before meetings of government planning committees in London. If the railroad service were accelerated, the contribution that Cambridge scientists make to national policy would be seriously diminished!)

To sum up: we in Britain are agreed that the policy to be followed in scientific institutions ought to be determined by scientists. We work on the assumption that policy proposals should originate in the laboratory and float upward as recommendations to be adopted by planning committees; directives from above downward should come, if at all, only as a consequence, as a sort of feedback, of recommendations that have floated upward. But this working basis for scientific policy in Britain leaves unanswered certain important questions. One is whether scientists should be detached from their laboratories to work full-time on policy-making for science, or whether the whole virtue of bringing scientists into planning and policy-making is that they are still doing science. The other question is at what point do policy decisions become political rather than scientific and therefore ought to be made by politicians and not scientists. To take one example that recently was mentioned in the American press: the location of certain laboratories for government research. Should they be where the scientists want them, which may mean overconcentration—for scientists, like wolves, like to hunt in packs? Or should they be where the politicians want them, which may mean a scattering over the nation that is frustrating to the scientists? On rationalization of resources for higher education, we have, I hope, a lot to learn from recent moves among Midwest universities in America.

ministration (NASA), it is playing an increasing role in the development of either selected areas of universities, in the case of the NASA sustaining grants or the various NIH development grants, or the whole scientific area of the university, in the case of the National Science Foundation program. It is playing an increasing role, therefore, in the development of universities and an increasing role in the development of new scentific centers of excellence.

Again, the federal government maintains a large system of its own laboratories in agriculture, in the Atomic Energy Commission, in commerce, the Bureau of Standards, in the Department of Defense, where there are some 155 laboratories, and in NASA. Some of these are civil service laboratories, some are attached to universities, and some are operated by contract with industrial organizations or through universities. At the present time the federal government finances 90 percent of the research and development activities of the aerospace industries. This is a very important point, because so much of the federal R and D expenditures is in the aerospace industry that the problem in obtaining more R and D funds for the Midwest is not simply one of salesmanship—it is one of building airplanes and rockets. The federal government also finances about 75 percent of the research and development in the electronics industry as well as substantial but, in general, small proportions of the research and development in other major industries. It has still a further role. Through its purchases, and again particularly in defense and space, it provides a market for some of the most difficult to make and of the most advanced technological products, and this plays an important role in development. For example, the role of the government as a market has been at least as important as its direct contribution to R and D in the development of large-scale electronic computers. Increasing sophistication, increasing size, increasing memory capacity were very badly needed, especially in national defense problems, and in the early stages this provided a market for the manufacturers of such equipment, a market that preceded the development of the civilian market, which is now predominant, although the defense and space market is still a major one. I might note that it is this activity—this role of the market and the question of these indirect effects of the federal involvement—that have very much intrigued the European countries who are very much convinced, I do not know whether correctly or not, that our activities in esoteric fields, defense, and space have had a major effect on all of our industry.

This is sort of a short list and is by no means complete. In limited space it would not be wise to attempt to summarize the whole of the government activities, but I think that the points mentioned suggest the extent of federal involvement in our higher educational system and in our industrial system. The involvement is big enough so that federal policies and their changes have a major effect on big segments of education and of industry and on many parts of the country.

To do all of these things, the federal government now spends about $5 billion a year on research of which $1.1 billion goes to universities, and that does not count the fellowship and training grants and the educational rather than scientific activities. It is spending another $456 million on science education, including fellowships, traineeships, other training programs, and the increasing activity in curriculum development and course content in the various sciences. Aside from this $5.5 billion, another $10 billion goes into technological development, chiefly in defense and space. Altogether these expenditures amount to 15 percent of the federal budget; in fact, they amount to somewhat over a quarter of the disposable budget in any year after one takes out the fixed expenses. Certainly an activity of this magnitude involves major questions of public policy and needs the attention of the scientists and of the academic community as well as the attention it is receiving within the Executive Branch and increasingly in the Congress. The urgency of evolving sound policies is accentuated when one realizes that only twenty-five years ago the total federal activity in science amounted to only $75 million, one two-hundredth of that at the present time. It is growing at a very, very great rate, and we have got to learn to accommodate what we do at least as fast as it grows. These figures indicate that the federal involvement in science is relatively new. To be sure, the patent office was established in 1790; it was one of the early acts of the Congress. In 1807 Congress authorized President Jefferson to establish what is now the Coast and Geodetic Survey. During the middle 1800's Matthew Maury did a systematic charting of the ocean currents and winds (I guess this is an example of applied science for an aspiring sea power in the age of sail). The first expression of interest in science as science came with the founding of the Smithsonian Institution. This step, however, was, I might say, forced on the Congress. I shall here ignore the exact details, but the money was willed to the United States Government by an Englishman, and it took the Congress roughly fifteen to twenty years to decide to go ahead with it, even under those circumstances. Nevertheless, its charter says that it has the primary purpose of increasing and diffusing knowledge among men.

The first serious steps did not come until after the Civil War. At that time our great state universities had not been founded, and the private universities that led the way were little more than advanced preparatory schools. The first graduate schools were still twenty years in the future. Certainly most of the energies of the country were concentrated on binding the wounds of the Civil War, on conquering the West, and on erecting the great industrial base that has been the source of our wealth and strength. At that time we left it largely to Europe to make the discoveries in science that stimulated the new kind of industry that was beginning to be born, that was based on scientific advance. It was against this background that in 1862 Congress took a very wise, foresighted step in the Morrill Act authorizing each state legislature to designate a land-grant college to receive federal funds spent for the advancement of the agricultural and mechanic arts. Purdue University, of course, was one of the land-grant colleges. In 1887 the Hatch Act set up the magnificent mechanism of agriculture research stations at the colleges. As the research capacity expanded, the need of a system of applying the results became obvious, and in 1914 the Congress evolved the means—the county extension agent, who even now continues to serve the purpose of coupling the university research process to the practical needs of the farmer.

This is an important point, because in any national science policy one of the central issues is how one gets two ingredients simultaneously: a healthy basic research policy and a healthy mechanism for coupling the basic research to the needs of the society. One can quite imagine a society in which one had a very good basic research program in healthy universities that did not benefit at all the society in which it was buried. Others have worried equally that basic research can be swamped, in turn, by the immediate practical goals. The problem is to obtain a balance. In the Agriculture Act these problems were recognized at an early stage. One had a mechanism both of research and of transfer to the users. I might say that this extension service has also served as a model that is now being very much thought about as a means to transfer information to a diffuse group of small users. A lot of thought is going into analogous schemes for getting the results of research into the hands of small businesses and small industrial organizations. Because the results of research and even of technological development are not necessarily along the lines of the original undertaking, in general the small firms do not find it profitable to maintain research activities since the results of research, the benefits, often accrue to someone else. The amount of research undertaken tends to grow with the size of the organization, all other things being equal.

The yield from the federal investment in agriculture has been enormous. The land-grant colleges have prospered and are now a major part of the intellectual backbone of the country. The agricultural research and its effective utilization by the farmers have revolutionized farming in America—in Russia I have seen enormous contrasts —and have converted it from a traditional to a sophisticated and scientific occupation. In 1887 the labor of one farm worker fed six people. Today it provides food for 31. Put differently, 7 percent of our population now feeds us very well and, in fact, somewhat to excess. Whereas in most countries farmers are the most traditional and conservative people in their methods, the American farmer has quickly adopted fundamental changes such as contour farming. At present he eagerly looks forward to new types of seeds, to better fertilizers, and newer pesticides. He sends his sons to the state university to be trained in scientific agriculture. It seems to me this has been a model case, although it is an old one, that illustrates not only the importance of research to the society but especially of the transfer of the results of research to practice. It has been an investment many times repaid. It has been often cited that on hybrid corn the annual return on the total research costs has been of the order of 700 percent. Nevertheless, except for that early experiment and that successful experiment in agricultural science, there was not really any federal science policy in the years between then and World War II.

The modern role of the federal government in science certainly originated in the experiences of World War II. Through the Office of Scientific Research and Development and the National Defense Research Committee the forces of science and particularly academic science were harnessed to the needs of the war effort. Under the imaginative and forceful leadership of Vannevar Bush and James Bryant Conant the results were spectacularly successful. It was demonstrated that men schooled in the hard discipline of fundamental research were flexible and able to turn to new and unanticipated problems. They brought to bear on them the fruit of experimentation in many areas seemingly unrelated to practical problems of any sort. Nevertheless, they produced practical results that contributed essentially to the successful prosecution of the war. It became clear at that time that science and scientists were a national asset. The lesson was not lost, and a new phase began.

The postwar phase was characterized by a recurrent pattern. It involved features that continue to be repeated in military affairs, in health affairs, in atomic energy, and in other matters. The principal features are the following. First, there was the recognition that systematic research and development activities could further the goals and missions of an agency; these are the goals that are defined by an essentially political process. Indeed, in most cases it was clear, as in the rapidly evolving military technology, that the rapid application of new science was absolutely essential for our future and for survival. So this application of systematic R and D to the defined missions of the agency, to the defined goals of the government, was in each case the start. Second, there was a general recognition in all of these cases that the application of what is already known, either in an academic sense or as industrial state-of-the-art, would soon exhaust the resources being drawn upon. This led, in each case, to efforts to encourage the development of new technologies, new industrial skills, even in the absence of specific applications, and particularly to the encouragement of basic research aimed at unearthing new knowledge, discovering new phenomenon, creating new concepts, and achieving a new level of understanding.

What I have stated thus far is not new. This was recognized by advanced industries before the war, and, in themselves, these points would have led to the expansion and development of government laboratories and government development organizations. For instance, one might have carried on military development within the government. And to a considerable extent this did take place. But the peculiar flavor of the American evolution of federal science derived from some further points. It was recognized that the universities possessed a great pool of talent and that their help was vital to the future of the sponsoring agency. They needed to develop their research capability and even more their capability to produce students who could lead the way in the future. Their faculties in the meantime were drawn into the work of the agencies as advisors or consultants. And, what was most important to the pattern that was developed, the universities did not play their role by direction. They were not, in general, told what to do and what was needed to further the goals of the government. Instead—this is oversimplified, but it was the general pattern—the research contract and the research grant was, by and large, awarded on the basis of proposals that were originated in the universities by the scientists, who themselves perceived the new opportunities and who themselves were anxious to get on with the job, to seize opportunities and take advantage of them.

This, of course, meant that one was drawing ideas from the entire academic community, the entire intellectual and scientific community. In a similar way, and particularly in defense, the importance of utilizing the skills and talent inherent in our industrial organization was recognized. And again the particularly American way of doing it, which is only particularly American in the sense that it was not widely emulated, was to utilize the industrial research and development contract as a means of developing new weapons systems and also, later, space systems. Again it was based, at least in part in this case, on proposals that originated in industry. Again this had the effect of diffusing the thinking process from the bureaucracy out to the great pool of national talent.

Let us consider a specific example. The Office of Naval Research (ONR), I think, first developed this pattern of doing things. It already had a traditionally good laboratory in the Naval Research Laboratory, but it devised the research contract as a special new instrument that was not like the conventional contract in that it did not convey the notion of purchase of services. It developed the research contract as a special instrument for the support of research, particularly in universities. Realizing that the future of naval weaponry depended on progress in the entire range of sciences, ONR provided support and let contracts in fields ranging all the way from biology to physical sciences, mathematics, nuclear science, and engineering.

Consider another example. The federal government had been interested in health research even before World War II, but only one institute, the National Cancer Institute, had been established. After the war, however, the conviction by Congress of the federal responsibility for health research led to the successive establishment, first, of eight other institutes, then, four divisions, and a clinical center, which now comprise the National Institutes of Health. Again, this is an establishment to meet directly the immediate goals of the federal government, namely, the improvement of the health of our people.

Then, in 1947, suggested by the pattern established by ONR, the Division of Research Grants was established and was given the authority to institute training programs. This action marked the beginning of the great general build-up in health-related sciences in the medical schools, hospitals, and the universities. It marked the beginnings of a systematic effort to improve the numbers and the quality of the students trained. It marked the beginning of an effort by NIH to improve the number and the quality and the geographic distribution, I might add, of the institutions involved. At the present time, as a result of this, the magnitude of the external program is very much greater than the one conducted within the institutes. As the institutes and their external programs have proliferated, so too have the appropriations increased, climbing from about $3 million in 1946 to more than $1 billion in 1965.

I shall cite one other example of the same pattern. The Atomic Energy Commission was established by the Congress, in the first place, to further nuclear weapons development and, in the long-run, for a more important purpose, to develop the peaceful uses of atomic energy. This again is a defined goal. To carry out this mandate the Atomic Energy Commission not only built up major laboratories and facilities of its own, but it turned to the universities. It helped to foster university activity in all of the sciences, from biology to mathematics, chemistry, physics—in all the fields that underlie nuclear science and technology. Similarly it fostered industrial activity in the areas related to its mission. In the universities, for example, it did so by setting up laboratories at universities and through research contracts, and, for a period, it awarded fellowships.

So this general evolution from a goal established in the government, then to specific research and development programs to further that goal, and then finally to the support of large areas of general science that underlie the specific areas in which the agency is involved—this has been repeated over and over again, and it is essentially, one might say, the prevailing pattern now. It was repeated most recently in our space program, which started out at a much later date. We have managed to evolve a government-industry-university triumvirate that has as its main characteristic agency programs oriented toward specific goals. The establishment of those goals is, by and large, not a problem of the scientific community, although the scientific community, of course, plays a major role in pointing out the opportunities and the feasibilities and so on, but it involves the entire body politic. There are primary agency programs, and they are conducted according to their nature in any one of the three: within the government, in universities, or industry. There are programs in addition, though. In each of the agencies, there are programs in support of general scientific and technological advance over broad areas related to the primary program. For example, the NIH supports research in all health-related areas. Naturally, the center is in the life sciences, but it extends to organic chemistry, to biophysics, and even to mathematics. One needs lots of very sophisticated statistics to understand biological systems, for example. A subsidiary effect of one of these programs is that now many of the agencies in the government have acquired a direct interest in university development and the training of advanced students.

One of the other features of the federal system, as it has evolved, is that it is now characterized by a complicated advisory network—in fact, too complicated to describe and which magazine articles have made fun of. In this advisory network industrial and, particularly, university scientists—and there has been an enormous involvement of university people, incidentally, not only in science but also in economics and the social sciences—participate very directly in the operation and formulation of the agency programs. As to the geographical origins of the President's Science Advisory Committee mentioned in other papers, let me state that the 1965 appointees to the President's Science Advisory Committee came respectively from St. Louis, Missouri, from Houston, Texas, from Boulder, Colorado, from California—a reasonable geographic distribution.

The only agency in the government that was established by law with the responsibility for the health of general science and for science education, the National Science Foundation, provides only 13 percent of the support of academic research and only a slightly greater proportion of the support of students. This is important to realize because the Congress frequently forgets it. At the present time, all of the agencies have an important role. There is a strong temptation to cut the budget of the Department of Defense because it is spending so much on education, which is not the business of defense, it is said. But unfortunately, since defense supports about 31 percent of the academic research, there has not always been a corresponding disposition to put it back into the National Science Foundation, for example. I might note on that score that in the 1965–66 budget, we looked for the first time at an over-all pattern for the agencies. Since there is going to be a growth of 10 percent in the school population in 1966, and an increase in costs, we provided in the budget for a 15 percent total increase in the funds for the support of university research and education. This was reflected in a major increase in the National Science Foundation budget to which most of the new increase went.

This system has provided a diversity of sources from which most academic research projects, and many industrial projects, may be funded. As a result, many agencies play related and sometimes competing roles in many of these areas. More than half a dozen, for instance, offer substantial support to university science and to the training of scientists. At least five federal agencies now play considerable roles in oceanography, for example. And I could mention a number of other such fields. This diversified approach to science, based on goals or missions that have been identified through the political process, but with a shared responsibility for the general scientific base, has been an enormously successful one. The vitality of American science and of American industrial technology has been great in these last twenty years, whether it is measured by Nobel prizes, by the desire of foreign scientists and engineers to come to this country, or by the concern which is being shown in Europe for the rapid progress of our industry in the most advanced technologies.

Of course, I want to point out that simultaneously we are also being pressed by Western Europe and by Japan in many other areas of technology. But in some of the most advanced fields, for example the field of computers, we have taken a leading role. In my opinion, there has been an extraordinary change in the quality as well as the quantity of the work done in our universities. Their attention has been directed toward research in a way which could scarcely be imagined before the war, except in a few places. Whereas then research and graduate education were an integral part of only a few universities, now it is generally recognized that a university cannot attract and hold a first-rate faculty unless it provides opportunity for scholarship and research. And the stimulus of science has aided, at least in the universities I know, all the university departments. It has awakened and stimulated our people. It has opened up new intellectual horizons as new discoveries are made in high energy physics or in the genetic code. It has kindled interest in the interior of the earth, in the oceans, in the atmosphere, and in outer space. It has made boldly evident the possibilities inherent in the continuing scientific revolution. Nevertheless, questions have arisen. They have arisen concerning the magnitude and the rate of growth of this program. I note that it is not only that R and D constitute 15 percent of the budget but that the expenditures have been doubling every seven years. Just this size and rate of growth have made the whole scientific and technological program of the federal government sufficiently important to warrant attention from the Congress and stimulate public discussion and symposiums.

One of the principal questions that has arisen is whether the superposition of separate agencies programs, with each making separate decisions as to their focus and emphasis and with programs considered separately by different committees of the Congress, can add up to a coherent whole that meets the nation's needs. One of the primary reasons for setting up the Office of Science and Technology, of which I am the director, was to achieve a certain degree of coordination, a sense of coherence and wholeness in our national program. Although this office was established in 1962, I cannot say that the federal program has yet been integrated, although progress is being made. One might say, in the language of the Supreme Court, that we are proceeding with all deliberate speed. I think it might be better, though, to say that we are feeling our way. There is a reason for it. The programs of the last twenty years have produced such vitality, they have made such progress, that we have no intention of killing the goose that laid the golden egg for the sake of greater administrative neatness.

I spent several weeks in Russia in November, 1964, looking at their industrial research and development program. There are very good people; there are very good laboratories; and what I saw was a very well organized system that could assign its priorities, that could say what was needed to be done and could put people to work to do it. What I also perceived was that it did not match in performance our somewhat less tidy way of doing these same things; in particular, it lacked the sense of entrepreneurship. We have generated what I have thought was a considerable sociological revolution in the universities, by which young men who had a good idea could go out and get themselves support and do something about it, and which did not rely entirely on the establishment of which they were a member, on their superiors and colleagues. And certainly the fact that our young scientists in universities, and to some extent in industry, have had the freedom to make their own decisions as to whether they spent money on a piece of apparatus or on a trip to a scientific meeting has had a great effect on the spirit of American science—even if by going to ask their department chairman, they could have made the trip to the meeting anyway. I was a department chairman for a while, and I could see what a difference it made to a man when he could make these decisions himself.

In this matter our viewpoint differs from that of almost all of the European governments. They have all stressed and focused on the problem of the allocation of resources, the development of rational priorities, and the importance of a plan for scientific advance and development. I consider that the most important feature to be preserved in our system is the dynamism I have mentioned, the creativity of the individuals in the organizations, the entrepreneur spirit of our industrial enterprises, of the individual scientists, and of members of research laboratories. There can be little question that the diversity of our approach, the use of competing alternatives, the use of the proposal as a primary instrument to solicit ideas from many sources, and the involvement of a large part of the scientific community in programs formulation have all contributed to the *élan* that has characterized this last twenty years in American science. Naturally, we not only want to be, we intend to be prudent and wise in our expenditures, but my point is that the problem is one of making sound investments. Good investments pay off well, and it is demonstrable that up until now our investments in our technological and scientific advance have paid off. The economists tell me that about two thirds of the growth in our national product can be accounted for in terms of technological advance; so that the primary problem is to continue to make sound investments that will pay, rather than to consider science as an expense that must be carefully trimmed into shape. When I say science, I include industrial technology.

Having stated all of this, I am going to put on my prophetic hat, which is dangerous, and try to take a look at where I think we are going. There are going to have to be changes. It is quite plain that we cannot continue forever the rate of growth, for example, that we have maintained since World War II. A series of questions have been raised and are being studied on many fronts. The Congress, through the Select Committee on Government Research (the Elliott Committee) and through the Subcommittee on Science, Research, and Development (the Daddario Committee), which is a subcommittee of the Science and Astronautics Committee, have conducted excellent hearings on the nature of federal science policies and their impact. The Elliott Committee has published ten very good reports, the Daddario Committee has published five. The question of science and public policy is becoming so popular that a large library of reading matter is developing. The problems that are becoming increasingly important, now that this has become a large system that affects the whole country and affects our industry, raise regional questions. For instance, what level of research should the country support in order to maintain our leadership and to achieve the goals that we set for ourselves? Another question: By what mechanism, if we are going to limit the expenditure and not just grow as the opportunities present themselves, do we rationally decide what the relative priorities are among, for instance, fields of science? Of course, I could ask: How do we rationally decide among the various social goals? That, of course, is the business of the political process, but we have never evolved anything corresponding to that within the main corpus of science.

The question of wasteful duplication is now raised widely. This question is often misstated because it views science as a process by which you go simply from here to there, so, if two people state the same goal, this becomes duplication. I suppose the best analogy as to what is wrong with this approach is that, if two people try to solve the problem of a maze, in a certain sense they are duplicating efforts, but the odds are very good that the problem will be solved sooner if two devote themselves to it than if one does. So, in many circumstances, it is good policy, when there is a puzzle to be solved, to have more than one effort and, of course, this is really what characterizes most research—problem-solving. Quite aside from the problem of wasteful duplication, it is also quite clear that one does not proceed in the best manner toward a goal by having separate and uncoordinated efforts, for example, to develop and improve universities, or to provide science information systems, or to carry on oceanographic programs. In the oceanography program, what is characteristic of the present situation is that the Navy makes measurements of temperature, currents, and salinity all over the oceans because it needs to operate submarines and ships on the oceans; the information and the scale of its program, therefore, is determined by military need and not by the needs of a national oceanography program. On the other hand, once these measurements have been made, they are available to the rest of the scientific community and certainly this fact cannot be ignored in planning other programs. Similar problems come up in developing the water resources of the country. There are problems of water pollution, or, in connection with irrigation, problems of water distribution; there are problems of how salt and silt flows when one diverts water from rivers and spreads it over land. These various problems are solved in several places in the government; they are independent, and this is proper. It produces a diversity of points of view; but, again, it does not make any sense to have many agencies have water sampling networks along the same river, one to measure salt, one to measure bugs, and so on.

A more particular problem that has become particularly acute is that of the geographical distribution of our efforts. This is a particularly difficult problem because one of the bases of the strength of our effort until now has been utilizing the scheme of proposals, judged on the basis of their merit. Also, it is demonstrable, contrary to what is sometimes asserted, that this process has resulted, during the period in which federal funds have expanded, in a diffusion of scientific strength in this country. Prior to World War II the concentration of scientific strength in some areas, primarily the two coasts and the region around the Great Lakes, was even more marked than at present. By any measure, one sees distribution taking place. Nevertheless, as it has become clear that there is a relation between the industrial climate and the scientific climate of the areas in the country, there has been a strong feeling that this has not gone fast enough. Most of the imbalance that is referred to occurs in connection with defense procurement. This was a very particular problem, not a generalized problem of procurement. It was largely procurement in the aerospace and electronics industry and mainly a problem of procuring, under pressure, ballistic missiles. Everyone remembers the missile gap, when the emphasis was on producing new weapons in the shortest possible time. The present pattern was largely dictated by purchases from the aerospace industry where the aerospace industry was. This does not say that it should stay that way to all eternity, but here, just as in the case of university science, the question is how to balance the delays and losses that come by insisting on transfers from where strength already is against the longer term gains of spreading the base.

Our policy at the present time, in the case of the universities, has been stated by President Johnson, and it is clearly to spread the scientific base. We want good universities, and this means we also want good faculty research, good academic research, in all parts of the country. In the course of achieving this, in the course of building up new centers, in the course of strengthening universities though, we do not intend in any way to diminish the quality of the strong institutions that already exist in all parts of the country. We must not cut back on the strong institutions that set the standards and the tone for the whole enterprise. One must never neglect, both in industry and in the universities, the importance of the standard that has been set by those places and by those people who are doing the most difficult problems at any given time. On this problem, incidentally, I should note that the distribution of funds from the National Science Foundation and the National Institutes of Health does approximate reasonably well the distribution of population, except for a few parts of the country, notably the South and Southeast. The Midwest actually fares very well on that score. This problem of achieving a better geographic distribution, particularly in the development programs, is certainly one that I anticipate we shall work on and make progress on.

One of the thorny problems to which all of the European countries have addressed themselves is the question of whether and how the results of federally sponsored research and development can be made to contribute to the civilian economy. In talking about the federal expenditures, it should be noted that practically none of them are made in connection with what I would call the great producing industries of this country—chemicals, textiles, metals, automobiles, and so forth. These industries largely carry on their own research and development programs. There are other industries, small industries, in other fields, in which the rate of technological advance has not been great. The question is what is the proper relation between the federal government and private enterprise in stimulating innovation and growth in our economy. It is clear that there are some matters, like setting standards, that are proper roles for the federal government. There is before the Congress the State Services Bill that makes a beginning, through the state universities, at setting up information services that will make the results of technological development available to local industry. I think this is a problem on which we should continue to work, because, if we are going to maintain the growth in our standard of living, we are going to have to continue to advance in the next twenty years as we have in the past.

Looking ahead, it seems clear to me that we are going to have to continue to expand the support of universities. We have more stu-

dents coming in. They are already in the high schools and the elementary schools, and, as the number of students grows, if we are going to
give the same quality of education, if we are going to provide the
same research opportunities, we are going to have to increase the investment, and an approximate 15 percent per year for some years to
come would seem to be a reasonable target. One can think of reasons
why it does not have to go up quite that fast, but, if we want to build
new centers of excellence, if we want to produce research in states and
places where there is none now, this will require added expenditures.

In addition to all of these things that are essentially administrative
problems, that say that we must do what we have been doing better
and more rationally and more coherently and that we are working on
ways to do it, I should also maintain that we must learn how to apply
science and technology to new areas, to new social goals, to new
possibilities. This is certainly going to happen. The most obvious one,
the most immediate one, is this whole question of the pollution of our
environment—the air, the water—by all the products of an industrial
civilization. We know very little about how to deal with these problems at the moment. There is very little work that has been done on
the toxicology of very low levels of continued exposures to many
kinds of pollutants. There is being developed now a major new environmental pollution program. Since any program on environmental
pollution interacts strongly with the industrial structure of our country and the economy, I think this is going to become an increasing
concern.

Another such problem, which is amenable to much more scientific
and technical analysis than it has been, is the whole problem of the
water resources of the country. Everywhere in the country, water is
becoming a scarce commodity. It has always been scarce in the
Southwest, but there is a plan, the Parsons Plan, for transporting
three times the quantity of water in the annual rainfall of the whole
western region of this country water down from the Canadian and
Alaskan Arctic. But this is not going to happen overnight. Present es-
timates are that it will cost approximately $100 billion, and our
experience with all other major programs would tell us that, without
having looked at any figures, if the rough estimate is $100 billion,
the correct amount will be more like $300 billion. It may sound ab-

surd to talk in such figures. But let us remember that this country now spends $50 billion a year on its defense program and, if we come to a stage where the nation, and I wish it were so, could dispense with the effort it is now devoting to its defense and its security, then we are actually only talking about an effort equivalent to a few years of the defense effort. With such efforts and such expenditures, one can begin to talk about remaking the structure of a continent. As soon as one has said this, I think one realizes that, if we ever devote the kind of effort that we devote to military problems to the solution of other problems, the possibilities are that we can think of a scale of effort that we have never been able to think of before. Similarly, the atmosphere of the earth, as one would like to believe as we learn more about its total circulation patterns, is amenable to control and modification. The day is surely far away, but we have never really attacked this as a major problem. The possibilities again are enormous, and the impact is enormous. It has been estimated that it would net this country $7 billion a year just to extend the reliable period of weather prediction to one or two weeks.

Finally, there is a problem that is going to be attacked more vigorously—transportation. In the past the federal government has been nearly the sole supporter of transportation by air, and the supersonic transport will be another example of this support. On the other hand, for our entire transportation system, which is sharply divided by modes, a good intellectual, analytical base has never been developed, either in the industry or in the government, for looking at the system as a whole. We have invested really tiny amounts of money in dealing with it as a whole system. As you know, the government is making a start in 1965 at doing research and development on the technical means of high-speed ground transportation, as an example.

Lastly, all of our progress depends, I think, on the education of our people, not only scientists and engineers but citizens who understand what the implications and the role of science and technology are. I think that we have finally realized the importance to all of our activities of the educational system, the importance of devoting to the educational system at least a small fraction of the kind of research effort that we make in other areas—which is systematically to apply thinking to the improvement of the education system. I think that we can look forward now to a major effort not only on the expansion of educational opportunity but the development of a more systematic approach to the question of what constitutes education, how the learning process takes place. Maybe we will even learn how to train an engineer. Recently I have attended violent debates as to whether engineers should become more scientific or whether engineers are so scientific that they do not appreciate what the problems to be solved in a real society are anymore. To that I have no answer.

I think it is quite clear that the federal government is in the science field to stay. Let us also note that the private sector also contributes about $6 billion to the research and development that is most closely connected with our productive industries, and anyone who really wants to think about this problem of geographical distribution and what it connotes for the areas of the country would do well to investigate the geographical distribution of the private expenditures on research and development.

J. Edward Roush

THE CONGRESS

IN INSTITUTION BUILDING

As a representative of 460,000 residents of the State of Indiana I have long since learned that, in addition to representing these people, there is an even larger responsibility imposed on one serving in the United States Congress—the responsibility of serving the over-all national interest of this country. In the past few decades this responsibility for the members of the Congress has increased because of the involvement of the federal government in so many areas of endeavor.

In this paper I have been asked to present the "Congressional view" of science and the university. I am very much aware of the significance of this Congressional responsibility. My primary committee assignment is to the House Committee on Science and Astronautics. This committee was established on July 21, 1958, and became during the next, or 86th, Congress a standing committee. As such, it exercises legislative jurisdiction with "across-the-board" jurisdiction. It exercises jurisdiction over outer space, including exploration and control thereof, science scholarships, and scientific research and development.

It also exercises legislative jurisdiction over astronautical research and development, including resources, personnel, equipment, and facilities, and over the following executive agencies of the government: The National Bureau of Standards (including standardization of weights and measures and the metric system), The National Aeronautics and Space Administration (NASA), The National Aeronautics and Space Council, and the National Science Foundation. The committee is the only committee of Congress with general jurisdiction in the field of science.

Because of its responsibilities in the field of space, the committee has been forced to concentrate a major share of its attention to this complex area. However, in 1964 the Subcommittee on Science, Research and Development, whose major focus was science per se, was created, and thus an important step was taken toward meeting other responsibilities of the full committee. Objectives laid down for the subcommittee included:

(1) The over-all evaluation of scientific research and development throughout the country.

(2) The strengthening of Congressional sources of information and advice in the field of science and technology.

(3) The achievement of the most effective utilization of the scientific and engineering resources of the United States in the effort to accomplish national goals which affect the lives of all Americans.

(4) The Congressional oversight of the National Science Foundation.

In brief, the subcommittee has a mandate to focus its attention on science and technology, on the many administrative and operational facets of science in its relationships to government, as well as on specific scientific disciplines and interdisciplinary approaches to serve government and national needs. This subcommittee, of which I am a member, has spent many weeks and months considering the broad issue of geographic distribution of research and development funds—a matter I shall return to later in this paper.

I am also a member of the House Subcommittee on Advanced Research and Technology, and, early in 1965, this subcommittee devoted its attention to the scientific core of the program of the National Aeronautics and Space Administration. This program, calling for the expenditure of more than a quarter of a billion dollars, includes space vehicle systems, electronics, advanced power sources, nuclear rockets, chemical propulsion, and aeronautics.

Looking back through the years as an original member of the House Science and Astronautics Committee, the growing understanding in the Congress of science and technology is impressive. The hearings process has been sharpened by the improved level of questioning by Congressmen as well as the more expertly prepared and presented testimony from executive agency witnesses.

Some changes have been made to strengthen our committee. Technically trained, full-time consultants have been added to the staff. A Science Policy Research Division has been established by the Library of Congress. This new division serves as an aid to Congress in the analysis of issues and preparation of factual background material and as a bridge to the entire scientific community, which at one time seemed so isolated and so far away.

To me this represents tangible evidence of the clear recognition by the government that science has a vital role in policy. And we shall continue to equip ourselves for competent analysis of the $15 billion annual investment which our government makes in research and development. The days when the legislative branch had to depend on faith in authorizing and appropriating money for science-based activity have come to an end.

In illustration of this let me review briefly one of the issues that came before our committee and the alterations made in the area of advanced propulsion development. During the hearings on this issue the committee was able to establish that the Budget Bureau's action to eliminate the large, 260-inch, solid-propellant motor and the liquid-hydrogen-fueled M-1 engine was inconsistent with the national need for additional booster capability. It is possible the Congress will act to provide the funding to reinstate these two programs. Congress has sometimes been accused of "project engineering from Capitol Hill." This is not the case here. Rather it demonstrates an ability to understand the planning and management of large research and development programs in the same way Congress deals with other federal agency operations.

My interests in federal research and development funding, especially the NASA program, has brought home to me the vital interdependency of the federal government and our colleges and universities. NASA Administrator James Webb stated recently: "Most of the experiments carried aboard NASA satellites and deep space probes represent the work of scientists and engineers within the university community."

In the fiscal year beginning July 1, 1965, the federal involvement with our colleges and universities amounts to $4 billion. This includes construction, training, student support—and research and development. Practically one half of this amount, $2 billion, is for research and development in the schools and in the research centers administered by the schools. There are some instances in which federal funds represent 50 percent of all the income at some schools. Forty-two separate departments, agencies, and bureaus now have education-supporting programs of one sort or another. Twenty-eight federal entities support science and engineering in universities.

The NASA sustaining university program grew out of our recognition of this vital interdependency. The training grants are made to universities rather than to individual students. This fundamental concept is designed to strengthen the authority of the institution by the acceptance of these federal funds. The components of the plan—training, facilities, and research—have allowed many universities to contribute to the NASA objectives even though they were not prepared to engage directly in the sophisticated experimentation with satellites and space probes.

As of February, 1965, 886 pre-doctoral traineeships were occupied in the sustaining university program. Only twelve trainees have been removed because of academic failure. This certainly indicates to me that the universities have done an excellent job of trainee selection. It is expected that the yield of PH.D. scientists and engineers will reach an eventual total of one thousand per year.

The expanding relationship between the federal government and the university has not evolved without criticism. There have been recent charges that federal funding is a threat to the cohesiveness and to the integrity of science and the universities. There are serious imbalancing influences that will bear close watching. But other evidence shows quite the opposite effect.

The multi-disciplinary character of space science and technology has made it necessary that ideas and individuals cross conventional, departmental boundaries frequently and with ease. NASA research programs on campuses serve as a focal point for drawing together the necessarily diverse research activities. It seems to me, in the space program at least, that specialists are talking to one another about mutual problems in a manner that would not have arisen otherwise.

There is one hazard that is of concern to me and my colleagues on the science committee. Many of the government-supported technology programs by their very nature have a glamorous aura. They assume a prestige position in the eyes of the public as well as in the scientific community. And a second aspect of federal support is that it often involves expensive tools. The net result of these two factors could lead to a distortion of interest of faculty and students away from what may be equally important fields of science, fields of science that may be just as important to the future progress of society.

We hear of certain industries that are noninnovative or technologically backward. We hear of fields of science that are "poor relations" of molecular biology, high energy physics, and space engineering. If we let scientific glamour and expensive, elaborate facilities unduly influence the choice of careers and research projects, then both universities and our society will surely suffer. Our civilian industrial technology must be adequately served with first-rate scientists and engineers. The NASA fellowship program was designated, in part, to replenish the supply of manpower that would be taxed by the space program.

Keeping this potential threat in mind, it is interesting to review the proportion of doctors' degrees that have been awarded in the basic and applied sciences over the period of 1953 to 1963, according to a study made by the Department of Health, Education, and Welfare. Although the total number of doctors' degrees granted each year has climbed about 50 percent, the percentage awarded in the life sciences, engineering, mathematics, and physical sciences has remained almost constant. It has changed from 49 percent in 1953 to 49.3 percent in 1963.

While all this was taking place, think of the change in the role of science in our culture during that period. In 1957 the Soviet Sputnik galvanized us into a period of discussion and action regarding education that might never have occurred in the ordinary course of events. We became amazingly sensitive to education and its processes. At the same time, salaries and prestige for scientists began to rise. A recent poll conducted for the National Science Foundation revealed that on a prestige basis the scientist ranks third behind Supreme Court Justices and physicians. Incidentally, Congressmen share seventh place with college professors. What counteracting, intermingled forces stabilized the choice of vocation by our college students in the face of this tremendous emphasis on science? I cannot answer the question, but I think it is an intriguing subject for further thought. It also belies the charge that our schools have capitulated to technology.

Another point I should like to emphasize is the need for continuing close contact between university administrations and both the executive and legislative branches of the federal government. Imbalances that arise due to federal funding may not always be apparent to us in Washington. There is a recent example where clear communication and good faith are combining to rectify a problem thrust on the schools by federal support.

I refer to the limitation of indirect costs allowed in research grant programs. In 1964 the House Science and Astronautics Committee held hearings on this subject. University witnesses clearly established that an arbitrary ceiling on indirect costs distorts the accounting system, diminishes the financial resources of universities, diverts the capability of supervisors, and, most of all, is not a true measure of efficiency or research accomplishment.

In 1965 the President's budget contained a sentence that I believe is a direct result from the frank testimony of the universities and the recommendations of the committee's report. The President said: "I recommend that Congress remove its restrictions on payments to universities for the indirect costs of research grants."

As a result, in April, 1965, my committee chairman, Representative George Miller, and my subcommittee chairman, Representative Emilio Daddario, testified before the House Independent Offices Subcommittee on Appropriations in support of legislation that would provide for uniform and equitable overhead payments to all recipients of federal grants.

This shows most clearly how attention can be focused on a problem that the universities are agreed upon, so that it is widely discussed and then brought for action to the government.

The institutions of higher learning are constantly alert to their responsibilities. They have demonstrated prompt action can prevent awkward problems from arising. A recent example is contained in the statement of the American Council on Education, "on preventing con-

flict of interest in government-sponsored research at universities."
The statement stems from the increasingly complex relationships between universities, government, and industry.

Faculty members may be put in the position of gaining knowledge through the expenditure of public funds that creates a problem when they carry out other activities, such as a consulting arrangement with a private business. The transfer of knowledge and skill from the university to industry is a valuable mechanism for technology utilization. However, all recipients of government-sponsored work should be ready to assure one another and their institutions that no situation would arise that would bring their objectivity into question. The orientation of research, the purchase of supplies or equipment, the transmission of privileged information, and the influence in negotiation of contracts are potential hazards.

But, on the other hand, any regulation of the faculty must not infringe on the freedoms that traditionally characterize a university and its staff. Donald Hornig, the President's Science Advisor, has stated: "The Federal agencies are prepared to use the principles enunciated in this statement as a guide to their policies and practices in this area. . . . The greater the degree of responsibility accepted and exercised effectively by colleges and universities, the fewer detailed rules and regulations will the Federal agencies have to impose." The "jet-set" professor must not become a symbol of federal-funded science.

As a final observation, I would like to touch on the subject of geographical distribution. My colleagues and my constituents are probably well aware that I have made a series of speeches on the floor of the House of Representatives on this subject. I have called attention to the well-documented fact that some areas of our country are receiving a grossly disproportionate share of federal research and development funds. This disproportion is demonstrated whether statistics are compared on the basis of geography, population, numbers of scientists, or industrial productivity. I believe it is a question in the national interest. I have offered an amendment to the NASA authorization bill to increase the attention paid to the factor of equitable distribution in NASA research and development contracting. In a discussion of this subject, there is always the risk that the argument will be advanced that it is mere pork-barrel politics. I think a careful reading of my remarks will show it is the national interest, not regional pride, that is in danger.

There is absolutely no intention on my part to change the primary emphasis on competence. This must always be a major factor in allocating federal funds. What I maintain is that there are other factors that should be considered, such as that the diverse benefits of scientific activity should be available broadly throughout our population.

There is no apparent difference in the ancillary benefits of science to a community whether the funding source is private enterprise or government. But today, with the federal government providing 70 percent of all the research and development money, we find government contracts are the dominant influence on the distribution pattern. Since this is the case and will continue to be because of the prospect of new discoveries, horizons being lengthened, and no diminishment of federal involvement in sight, then the policy precedents we set now should be precedents that will best serve the national interest. I am reminded of the poem by Sam Walter Foss entitled "The Calf-Path."

> One day, through the primeval wood,
> A calf walked home, as good calves should;
> But made a trail all bent askew,
> A crooked trail as all calves do.
> Since then two hundred years have fled,
> And, I infer, the calf is dead.
> But still he left behind his trail,
> And thereby hands a moral tale.

The trail was then taken by a dog, then a sheep, until a path was made, and the path became a road, a village street, and finally a city thoroughfare.

> And o'er his crooked journey went
> The traffic of a continent.
> A hundred thousand men were led
> By one calf near three centuries dead.
> They followed still his crooked way,
> And lost one hundred years a day;
> For thus such reverence is lent
> To well-established precedent.

Forgetting the path of the calf, let us play the part of the lawyer, and look for acceptable precedent to uphold and sustain our case.

The portion of federal science funding having to do with universities is particularly important. The first major involvement of the government with science and education is the Morrill Act of 1862. This gave each state 30,000 acres of land or its equivalent for each United States Senator and Representative. The proceeds were to be devoted by the states to at least one college where the leading object should be, "to teach such branches of learning as are related to agriculture and the mechanic arts." The federal support of university research programs began with the Hatch Act of 1887. This established agricultural research stations at the land-grant colleges. A most recent example of federal involvement in science and education was the National Defense Education Act of 1958. This called for more scientific and engineering manpower as essential to our national defense.

You will note that the thread of logic running through these programs is equitable distribution of federal funding to accomplish goals for all of our society through an enhanced university science and engineering program. I maintain that the benefits of the $15 billion federal research and development program is in many ways identical with the side effects of the former programs and that a reasonable portion of research and development contracts and grants should be distributed in a like manner.

I should like to mention at this point that research and development are becoming more carefully separated in our minds, and they should be. The convenient abbreviation, R and D, is still useful but certainly does not refer to a single entity.

To return to the question of distribution, I should define equitable, in one aspect, as resisting the concentration of federal investment in a few areas or to a few universities. Scientists are highly mobile. Much of the work of science can be done anywhere in the United States. The presence of scientific activity attracts additional research and development to that region. What results is the well-recognized geographical clustering around Boston, Washington, San Francisco, and Los Angeles. This agglomeration is not accidental. It results from several economic factors, including the cooperative use of expensive laboratories, computers, and nuclear reactors and also the ready exchange of information and employees among research laboratories in a cluster. This makes the whole complex more viable.

As an illustration, in 1963 about $1.5 billion in federal research and development funds went to universities and their associated research centers. California received about $427 million, almost 28 percent. In the fiscal year 1962, the National Science Foundation awarded 4,791 fellowships. The University of California and the California Institute of Technology received 491, more than 10 percent. This demonstrates most clearly that the federal expenditure for research and development results in a flow of both talented students and faculty from less favored parts of the country. It results in further accelerating the concentration of expertise.

Some have said that the most important economic benefit to a region can come from applying new technology in a production operation. If this is the case, a region does not have to have a research and development center in order to benefit from federal funding. The Aerospace Research Applications Center at Indiana University, a technology utilization program sponsored by NASA, is an interesting experiment. It may well prove that industry in the Midwest can profitably use innovations from the space program, regardless of their origin. But I do not yet consider it probable that a highly technical industry will continue to remain or to locate in a region where there is no ready availability of research and development talent.

It is inconsistent with the former progress of our country in overall standard of living and intellectual climate to resign ourselves to the regional changes fostered by a hands-off policy of federal science funding. If we become a nation where a few favored localities accumulate the best scientific talent, we will have unwittingly allowed science to be a party to a social calamity. It will be a calamity comparable to the problems of air pollution, water contamination, and other undesirable consequences of modern technology.

Considerable ingenuity will be needed to avoid this ultimate predicament. The opportunity for discussion leading to sound proposals in the public interest could be provided if the recommendation of the Subcommittee on Science, Research and Development is adopted. The report of this committee, issued on October 23, 1964, stated unequivocally that some corrective action on geographical distribution was indicated. We recommended "that a government-industry conference be convened by the White House at the first feasible moment to explore ways and means of distributing federal research and development funds on a more even geographic basis."

Our problems as they relate to science and technology and public policy are many. It is good that we have begun to seek solutions now.

When President Kennedy addressed the National Academy of Sciences he told the story of the great French Field Marshal Lyautey and his gardener as they discussed the planting of a tree. "But, sir," said the gardener, "it will not flower for a hundred years." "In that event," said Lyautey, "plant it this very afternoon."

John Brademas

A CONGRESSMAN'S PERSPECTIVE

I should like to present some aspects of science and technology and their impact on our society, and I shall do so from the viewpoint of a Member of Congress of a particular party who represents a particular district and who serves on a particular committee.

My perspective is that of a Congressman who represents a Midwestern district that has had certain economic difficulties in recent years (as demonstrated most obviously by the exodus of the Studebaker plant) as well as that of a member of the Congressional committee that writes most of the education legislation in the House.

I propose to discuss briefly the field of science and technology and to discuss some of the implications of scientific and technological developments for the Midwestern part of the United States.

First, let me observe that I think it is now widely recognized that scientists and engineers and their research and development activities played a crucial part in winning World War II. But today scientists and engineers are increasingly recognized by the public generally and by politicians in particular as essential to winning the future. For only in recent years has the country come to accept the critical role that scientists and technicians play in economic growth, the health and well-being of our people and in the overall strength of our nation.

I should like to concentrate on one particular problem in the field of science and technology about which a number of us in the Midwest have in recent years become increasingly concerned. I refer to what has been described, in a most inelegant if telling phrase, as the "Midwest brain drain."

I remember very well going in the summer of 1962 with a group of fifteen Midwestern Congressmen to the Office of Secretary of Defense

McNamara to discuss with him the problems occasioned by the flow of defense procurement contracts away from the Midwest to the East and West Coasts. You will recall, I am sure, the celebrated report, "The Changing Pattern of Defense Procurement," issued by the then Under Secretary of Defense, Roswell Gilpatric. Secretary McNamara told us during our visit that the shift would continue unless the Midwestern states and our local communities acted to develop our capacity for scientific research and technology.

This is the statement of the Secretary on that occasion: "We seek the best brains and we go where they are and generally speaking they are not in the Midwest."

Secretary McNamara was not, of course—as some Midwestern politicians either erroneously or deliberately represented him as doing—declaring that the Midwest was a desert of ignorance. He was, rather, describing a sociological fact; namely, that some parts of the United States have attracted scientific and technical manpower and research programs more effectively than we in the Midwest have done.

It was late in 1964 that this subject of the "brain drain" was translated into statistical reality in a report prepared for the House Science and Astronautics Committee. In this report we learned with dismay that the Midwest—here I refer to what the statisticians call the East North Central region, that is, the states of Illinois, Indiana, Michigan, Ohio and Wisconsin—received in the fiscal year 1963 less than 7 percent of the prime contracts and grants awarded by the federal government for research and development. Since this region contains 20 percent of the nation's population and contributes at least 22 percent of the Gross National Product, this mere 7 percent is a matter that demands the urgent attention of those who live in the Midwestern part of the United States and those who represent the Midwest in Congress.

I think one result of the study to which I have just made reference is the announcement made in April, 1965, by Senators Joseph Clark of Pennsylvania and Gaylord Nelson of Wisconsin that a Senate Labor and Public Welfare Subcommittee will hold public hearings on the impact of federal research and development policies on scientific and technical manpower. Senator Nelson has told me that he intends in these hearings to prosecute very vigorously the case of the Midwest for a greater share of the scientific installations and research programs funded by the federal government.

A closer examination of the Science and Astronautics Committee report shows something rather surprising: although only 5 percent of federal prime contracts to profit-making organizations go to the Midwest, our region receives some 14 percent of all contracts and grants to educational institutions. The universities are therefore doing three times as well as industry in an area of competition with great significance for economic growth. This is a striking contrast with California and New York, for example, where the percentage of contracts and grants to universities is less than that awarded to profit-making organizations.

We can trace the outlines of this pattern still more clearly by looking at the diffusion of R and D funds through the processes of subcontracting. The Space Committee's study made a start on this analysis by looking at the first-tier subcontracts under the ten largest prime contracts awarded in the fiscal year 1963 by the Department of Defense, the National Aeronautics and Space Administration (NASA), the National Science Foundation (NSF), and the Atomic Energy Commission. These results show a decidedly poorer performance by the Pacific Coast, for example, as a subcontractor than as a winner of prime contract awards, and a better performance by the Midwest. I strongly suspect that, if this analysis were extended to the tens of thousands of smaller contractors and suppliers, all of whom share in the federal R and D pot, the Midwest would come out rather well. Of particular significance is the fact that over one third of the first-tier subcontracts under National Science Foundation prime contracts went to the Midwest, twice as much as to the Pacific Coast. The importance of this fact is that NSF programs are not mission-oriented in the sense that a weapons system, a space satellite, or a nuclear reactor is.

Based on these studies one might put forth the following hypothesis: that the Midwest is exceedingly successful in obtaining non-mission-oriented basic research funds; that it holds its own in general university research, basic and applied; that it does very poorly in industrial development related to federal research and development problems; and that it does very well as a supplier of production items in support of federal R and D projects.

If this hypothesis is correct, we may be confronted by a problem rather different from the one that has received so much publicity. For our region—the five states previously mentioned—with 20 percent of the nation's population, contains over 20 percent of the nation's scientists and engineers, generates 21 percent of the nation's personal income, and, in 1960, generated 24 percent of the nation's industrial research manpower. If there is a "brain drain," perhaps it is in large part owing to the fact that the region contains a larger percentage of the nation's engineers and scientists, but this may, in turn, tend merely to underscore the accomplishment of the universities.

Let me turn now to a question that is building up an increasingly stiff political voltage. Is there a federal procurement policy to discriminate against the Midwest or any other area of our country? The statistics reflect the results of thousands of individual procurement actions, each necessarily based on technical and business judgments. Under these circumstances it may be an understandable reflex to demand a region's fair share of federal R and D funds. But it seems to me that, if this demand for a fair share, whatever that may be, should end, there we can expect little beneficial effect for our part of the United States. Perhaps we can put the real problem in a more succinct way; namely, does the Midwest really want federal prime contracts for research and development? Does Midwestern industry, do Midwestern banking interests, and does our community at large indicate its willingness to do what is necessary in order to obtain such contracts?

If, in fact, we in the Midwest are not being aggressive enough in this respect, what government decisions or actions can we take to improve matters? The problem was highlighted by former Under Secretary of Defense Gilpatric when he said, with respect to the states surrounding the Great Lakes: "Certain institutions, certain companies, and certain communities have been far more alert, more active, and more effective in their quest for defense contracts than others have been."

We all know that the Midwest has been heavily oriented toward the civilian market, toward the production of automobiles, steel, heavy machinery, an orientation that has made it the industrial heartland of the United States. We know as well, however, that the Midwest has not really made, at least in my judgment, aggressive enough efforts to obtain a larger share of the federal research and development market.

Perhaps it would be essential before we draw too many firm conclusions about the distribution of federal funds to undertake an analysis of proposals by Midwestern industrial firms to federal agencies for research and development contracts. How many have been made? How successful have they been? How many were solicited and how many unsolicited? Then we should compare these figures with similar ones for other parts of the United States.

There is another very disturbing feature that is not related directly to federal research and development expenditures but is generated locally and concerns the attitudes of a society toward its educated people. It is a factor that may help explain the "brain drain."

A recent study by the National Academy of Sciences contains an analysis of the PH.D. degrees granted by American universities from 1920 to 1962. The study shows that the great universities of the Midwest (the five states referred to above) were the source of well over one fourth of all the doctorates produced in the United States during the 1920s—a figure above that of any other statistical region of the country. In the 1960–61 period, our region was still producing over one fourth of the nation's doctorates and continued to surpass any other region. It had maintained itself during this entire time span. Especially gratifying has been the demonstrated growth of many of our educational centers since World War II. Today seven of the first fourteen universities in the nation in the granting of doctorates are located here in the Midwest—Illinois, Wisconsin, Michigan, Ohio State, Purdue, Indiana, and Chicago. This analysis shows that many fewer holders of PH.D. degrees are employed in our region than are educated here. Perhaps this is not surprising for it is characteristic of a great center of learning that it should attract people from all over the United States. But what is surprising and disturbing is that a smaller percentage of this group of highly educated people is employed in the Midwest than was born in the Midwest, and this is indeed a "brain drain."

An equally disturbing feature is that this is generally true not just of the natural sciences but of the arts and professions as well. One can understand the mobility of mathematicians, physicists, electronic and mechanical engineers, and others essential to programs in defense and space; they will understandably go to the laboratories and institutes where federal R and D funds are being spent. But I am most uneasy when I see this trend in the nonscientific fields of specialization that are not supported by federal research and development.

To insure that these figures represented a sufficient body of data to warrant some conclusions, I made another check of material from the 1960 census. I was again surprised to see that in each of the states of this area the percentage of the population with at least four years of college education fell below the national average. The deficits varied from 40,000 to 70,000 college graduates per state.

Such evidence as this enables us to draw some conclusions about our situation in the Midwest. In our region we have an enormous production capacity, a bulwark of the industrial strength of the country, producing highly complex products for world-wide markets based on constantly improving technology. Yet industry is not deeply involved in the federally supported sector of technical advances unrelated to its business. Here is a region of great universities and educational traditions with outstanding faculties and teachers and research workers and students from all over the land, working on the frontiers of science and engaged, over a broad front, in research efforts supported by federal funds. And here is a society, a community of people, supporting and supported by the great industrial establishment and universities of the region. Yet this region has not yet effectively linked with its industry and commerce the rapid changes that are occurring with increasing frequency across the entire spectrum of science and technology.

There is, therefore, an unhappy, if indeed not vicious, cycle apparently at work. The universities have not yet done an effective job of bringing to the community an awareness of the advances of modern science. The community has not been able to generate enough concern about using such advances to meet the need for industrial diversification and even greater economic growth. Nor has industry been aggressive enough in seeking from the universities new ideas to be exploited and new scientific discoveries to be translated into the technology on which the future economy of the region will depend. The problem of which I speak is, therefore, in no small measure one of education and communication.

The situation I have been analyzing concerns the Midwest, the region I know best; it represents, I daresay, a problem shared in one form or another by other parts of the United States, even those currently enjoying large outlays of federal research and development funds. This federal support of science and technology is not in itself the primary cause of the problem, serious as the geographical imbalance is. The failure to attract federal prime contracts in the Midwest is symptomatic of more fundamental difficulties. The significance of federal prime contracts for R and D does not lie principally in the amounts of money involved, attractive though the money is, but rather in the identification of where the dynamic scientific and technological leadership is now to be found in this country. It is this leadership that is the key today to the character of the science and technology that will open the industrial frontiers of tomorrow.

To prove my point, one need only look at the growth of the computer, electronics, and space industries. The character of the most advanced science and technology today will determine the map of the economic future, and it will mean the difference between industrial advance and industrial lag. No industry can hope to flourish in the future merely by continued application of present or past technology. Midwestern industry cannot hope to build its long-run future along the same lines as the present technological strength of other parts of the United States. We cannot really run another Route 128 through South Bend or even through West Lafayette. Nor can an industry hope to build its technological base without a continuing supply of the trained and creative manpower that is the source of this base.

The economy in the United States today is generally good, but changes are in progress at home and abroad. In 1953 the United States exported twice the value of steel mill products and twenty times the value of the automobiles that it imported; by 1962 we were exporting only 25 percent more in steel mill products and only two and one-half times the value of automobiles than we were importing.

In 1958 an estimated 55 percent, over half, of the establishments in our machine tool industry were obsolete.

Figures such as these—and they could be extended over a broad area—cannot be improved by the simple expedient of building more productive capacity. Nor can they be improved by waiting until the deterioration is obvious to all; for the training of people takes time as do the processes of innovation and the exploitation of new ideas.

The problem of innovation is, therefore, a national problem. The innovative capacity of the nation is a national resource. It is a resource so important to the well-being of the country that its allocation to specific tasks cannot be delegated, if you will permit a politician to say so, solely to scientists and engineers.

Part of this innovative capacity is now being utilized by the federal government alone. In a free society, with a free economy, the allocation of innovative capacity will be made through the choices of thousands of entrepreneurs and managers throughout the country and through the actions of thousands of scientists and engineers who seek to make their contributions to knowledge. Any region, any community, any university, or any company that fails to allocate wisely its innovative capacity correspondingly weakens the whole and hence the future strength of the nation.

I repeat that the Government alone cannot and should not determine this allocation. To attempt to do so would be to undermine the proven sources of our national strength. Yet it must also be recognized that what the federal government does makes an enormous difference. The Government must, in the national interest, do what is necessary to aid all regions and parts of the country that need and want assistance. In my judgment, however, the federal government still has a long way to go in developing a national policy of allocation of federal research and development funds—sound not only from the viewpoint of accomplishing specific missions essential to specific federal agencies, but sound as well in terms of the over-all scientific and technological and economic strength of the nation.

Let us hope that Senator Nelson's hearings will shed some light on this problem, and I hope he sheds some heat on the government decision-makers as well. For example, I applaud the National Science

Foundation program to develop centers of excellence throughout the land, but it is my understanding that NSF has not yet allocated the money for these centers for the fiscal year which ended in June, 1965.

As I have said, the federal government cannot and should not determine all the mechanisms of allocation and exploitation of scientific and technological resources. Such determinations depend ultimately on the citizenry and on their informed view of society and the world. It is here perhaps that the universities have chief responsibility; for they must insure that the citizens are informed.

Meeting the problems of technology and social change involves all sections of our country and all institutions, public and private. I should like now to suggest a number of directions in which we might seek solutions for the kind of problems I have raised.

Once again I shall refer to the Midwest for practical, not parochial, reasons; for the leaders of the Midwest have not been oblivious of these problems and they have already undertaken many constructive steps.

First, it seems to me essential that the research and innovative capacity of our area be brought together with the productive capacity and in such a way that both can benefit. I believe that the universities can and should exercise a large part of the initiative here. There are some things that the universities can do, some of which they are already doing and doing well and others that they are not doing that, it seems to me, they should be doing. For example, I should like to suggest that universities and colleges organize forums at the local level for continuing discussions between university and industrial leaders about how the resources of each can be more effectively exploited to the advantage of both and to that of the entire community.

Second, I believe that Midwestern universities—at least the larger ones—should organize a series of symposiums at which the top administrators of the university, together with their scientific and engineering deans and local industry and governmental leaders, could meet with a selected group of the top scientists, educators, and industrialists in the nation. The purpose of such a gathering would be to discuss the future of that particular area and that particular university; to consider just what area of scientific and technological expertise could be developed in that university. Such a group would look down the road, as it were, ten or twenty years and would try to make some intelligent judgments about what problems will need solving in the American society then, not today. Notre Dame or Purdue or Indiana or Illinois could then begin to formulate decisions about how they can make unique contributions to meeting future national needs, contributions not paralleled elsewhere, perhaps in the fields of biomedicine, or in transportation, or urban problems, or in marine engineering, or what have you. My point is that we in the Midwest need to think about shaping the future and we are not now thinking hard enough about it and our part in shaping it.

But deciding on how we are going to participate in molding the future is not enough. We in the Midwest must also show some "follow through" at both the university and the community level. For example, we must, far more effectively than we have been doing, support at our universities a first-class research staff that works closely with the local financial and industrial communities to win their understanding and support. We need also, I believe, to realize that, in a given university, we should seek to build excellence in at least one particular area rather than make an effort to populate each of the departments of the university with one big name professor and thereby build not excellence but mediocrity.

Let me reiterate that above all we must think: we must think about the future; we must think about the question of the long-run scientific and technical and hence industrial advance of the Midwest. And having thought, we must make decisions on where to place our efforts, and we must not leave the decisions to chance; we must organize. An instance of the kind of action we might take is the development by the universities of resident fellowship or extension programs for company executives and scientists. Consider, for example, the problems that will occur in this country if peace should break out, if there should be a major disarmament agreement between the United States and the Communist world. Many industrial firms in the United States have been engaged almost entirely in defense procurement and the chief talent of many of their executives has been their capacity for negotiating with federal procurement officials; they have not had to develop, therefore, the innovative instinct—the ability to develop productivity—that has been an essential source of the economic strength of the United States.

Another suggestion would be to encourage increased consultative participation by faculty members with local industry. Such specific action can go far in helping to break down barriers that still exist in many communities between town and gown and can establish a basis for cooperation between the universities and industry.

Certainly the universities should continue the fine start that has been made in the development of research centers such as the McClure Park at Purdue University, the Illinois Institute of Technology Research Park, and the Modern Research Industries Park at Urbana, Illinois.

I know that another promising project has been the early success of the NASA-supported Aerospace Research Applications Center, initiated by Indiana University for the purpose of providing technical information services to industry. I must remark with perhaps more candor than a politician should, that some of us from the Midwest suspect that NASA was in part at least moved to authorize the Aerospace Research Applications Center out here to keep some of the more vocal and critical Midwest Congressmen off the backs of NASA for not providing larger, more substantial contracts to our part of the United States.

Also to be congratulated is the Committee on Institutional Cooperation formed several years ago by the joint action of eleven universities of the area, including the University of Minnesota and the University of Iowa, for the purpose of improving "the educational and public services offered by fostering cooperation in instruction and research, particularly at the graduate level." Another active organization resulting from the initiative of universities in the region is the Great Lakes Industrial Council.

If the universities have responsibilities so too does industry. I have stated that I think one of the greatest dangers to industry in the Midwest is its failure to look far enough ahead. It has too often confused increasing present production capacity with developing future strength. The rate of technological advance is accelerating. The volume of competition in sophisticated technology is increasing. It takes time to diversify and time to build and exploit new markets. So Midwestern companies, to a greater extent than many of them are now doing, should aggressively build their applied research and development capabilities. Industry should also, far more aggressively than it is now doing, take the initative in seeking the assistance of the universities to identify new product opportunities, new areas of exploitation.

Finally, I believe that Midwestern industry should much more actively seek federal support for research and development. It is perhaps ironic that a northern Democratic politician should have to be preaching the gospel of free enterprise, of competition, to Midwestern industry. Yet on several occasions during my seven years in Congress, I have helped organize seminars and procurement conferences in my own Congressional district for the the purpose of making available to the industrial and business firms of my area the latest information on government procurement possibilities and encouraging them to get in there and fight for the business. Industry must become more aggressive, more competitive, more enterprising, if you please.

The community, too, has responsibilities. It is gratifying to see the beginnings of active civic sponsorship of such ventures as the Greater Ann Arbor Research Park and two new research parks in Wisconsin. But I think there are not enough such examples in the Midwest. Encouraging as such efforts are, moreover, research parks cannot remain as mere symbols of technological enlightenment. They must touch and affect the attitudes and aspirations of the entire community. Nor can research parks substitute for direct communication between the universities and the community or, by themselves, solve a basic problem, namely the response of established industry to the technological challenges of the future.

The federal government is increasingly concerned with the kind of problems I have been describing, for these problems are national problems. The innovative capacity of the nation is a scarce national resource, consisting primarily of educated men and women, many of whom have received their training at public expense, and at expensive installations, many of which have been purchased with public funds. The great innovative centers of the nation are of three types—

government-owned and government-operated, government-owned and privately operated, and privately owned and privately operated. Since these are the places where the innovative resources of the nation are utilized, the government has a role and an obligation with respect to each.

It is in the government agencies, and often with the cooperation of government-operated laboratories and installations, that the judgments are made and from which the federal research and development funds are distributed. The government must examine its procurement policies and procedures more carefully than, in my judgment, it has been doing to insure that alternative sources are considered, to insure that unused capabilities throughout the nation are sought and appraised, to insure that we are avoiding unwarranted concentration. I do not, for a moment, want to imply that federal procurement of research and development services should be distributed purely on the basis of geography. I do want to suggest, however, that the federal R and D investment should not be inadvertently unbalanced through the operation of procurement methods that could be improved.

In the case of government-owned and privately operated activities, different problems arise. Recently, we have become aware of the latest candidate in the category—a 200-billion volt proton-accelerator expected to cost as much as $300 million to install and as much as $50 million a year to operate. This machine, probably the most expensive single research facility ever planned, will affect the community in which it will be located in much the same way as the NASA installation at Huntsville, Alabama, has. Where this accelerator will be located and who will operate it thus become issues of the greatest public concern. Congress must examine this type of problem. The factors involved—site selection, availability and mobility of the necessary manpower, ways of assessing the relative needs of different communities, the nature of the most effective management instrument —must be evaluated by Congress to insure that the national interest will be served. For a problem of this type and magnitude cannot be resolved solely by the scientists themselves but only through the consensus of all of the interests that will be affected by the outcome.

The third class of activities, those which are privately owned and privately operated, also imposes responsibilities on the government, for it is certainly in the public interest that they too should flourish. In this area the problems revolve around communications among groups —the communities, the universities, and industry. Here, too, some of the problems must be examined by Congress—such problems as, for example, the management of scientific and technological information and the federal role in supporting education. Two items of legislation now pending before Congress offer significant promise in this area. They are (1) the Higher Education Bill and (2) the State Technical Services Bill. These bills complement each other. Part of the Higher Education Bill would enable universities, with government assistance, to establish or to improve community extension services and facilities, thereby providing a mechanism for drawing upon many resources of the university necessary for the solution of community problems.

The State Technical Services Bill, which would be administered by the Department of Commerce, would focus on industrial technology and thus supplement the general community services program in meeting specialized needs. These programs together would operate through the choices and decisions of the local communities and their institutions.

Another way in which the government could assist regional industrial development is to establish financial incentives to encourage local industry to engage in research and development. One way this might be done has been initiated in Canada where a tax deduction of 150 percent of the increase in expenditures for research and development, after the base year of 1961, is now permitted for individual companies. Especially for small business, which is unable to establish its own R and D laboratories, such a provision could go far toward enabling many companies to maintain constructive relations with research institutes and universities.

In conclusion, let me say that Congress is increasingly coming to grips with the kind of problems I have been discussing. But before I give an indication of some of the ways in which Congress is seeking, fitfully perhaps, to meet some of the responsibilities that scientific and technological advance have brought to our country, I must interject one particular word about the role of the universities in the picture.

It seems to me that university administrators and scientists must involve themselves, whether they like it or not, in a kind of national science politics if their institutions and their regions are to benefit. It is not insignificant that the first four science advisors to the President came from Ivy League colleges, nor is it beside the point that Frederick Seitz of Illinois was the only Midwestern member of the President's Science Advisory Committee (PSAC). This is the trend which was continued in the spring of 1965 when several terms expired and there was but one Midwesterner among the new PSAC appointees. I trust that no one will take offense if a politician takes note of the politics of science!

Congress is experiencing its own scientific revolution as evidenced by the efforts of the space and the atomic energy committees and their research and development subcommittees; by the work of the Elliott Committee; and by the hearings that Senator Nelson is planning to undertake. Look further, if you will, to what we in Congress have been doing to increase the national investment in educated men and women—the National Defense Act of 1958, and the many amendments that have followed; by the Higher Education Facilities Act and the Vocational Education Act, both of 1963; by the Manpower Development and Training Act; and by the Health Professions Educational Assistance Act, to name only some of the education bills we have been enacting.

President Johnson has given me a signed scroll on which are inscribed the words that he spoke when he signed the pioneering Elementary and Secondary Education Act of 1965. In his remarks President Johnson declared: "Those Members [of Congress] of both parties who supported the enactment of this legislation will be remembered in history as men and woman who began a new day of greatness in American society."

I am confident that, if we in the Midwest—businessmen and bankers, scientists and engineers, professors and politicians—begin now, more aggressively than we have been doing, to think, to decide, to act along some of the lines I have made bold to suggest we can begin a new day of greatness for Midwest America as well.

Harvey Brooks

THE EXECUTIVE BRANCH AS AN INSTITUTION FOR SCIENCE

The views I will express are personal and represent impressions derived from about seven years of close observations and involvement as an advisor in the Executive Branch decision-making for science. However, it is important to remember that the perspective is that of a nongovernment participant with his central concerns in university research and teaching. This view has the advantage of a certain measure of detachment but with it perhaps an excessive focus on the interests and needs of the university sector.

I should like to begin by making some observations on the general characteristics of the American federal science establishment. The first point is that research and development as a federal activity is largely imbedded in the mission-oriented agencies of our government. Only the National Science Foundation has a specific mission to advance science for its own sake, but it accounts for only about 10 percent of the basic research and less than 5 percent of all the research supported by the federal government, and indeed only about 12 or 13 percent of all the research financed in the universities. It follows from this that planning and budgeting for science take place primarily within individual agencies which are directly responsible to the President and to the Congress for their scientific, as well as their other, activities. Science is thus deeply imbedded in other government operations and, in my opinion, properly so. Perhaps if there is any one characteristic that distinguishes the American scientific enterprise from the European one described in Sir Eric Ashby's paper, it is this imbedding of the enterprise in the actual missions of the federal agencies. Support of general purpose research for broad national purposes has thus come about largely as a by-product of agency missions and that includes the research that is a necessary part of advanced academic training. So far, since World War II, this research "fallout" has been very successful because the general growth of the research and development budgets of the federal government has coincided with the growing needs for the training of scientists and the Congress has adopted a very enlightened attitude toward the relevance of research to the missions of the agencies and permitted a broad interpretation of this relevance.

Another point to keep in mind is that the American science establishment is largely the product of an unplanned organic growth—a series of pragmatic responses to specific needs as they appear. It has not been constrained by the necessity of fitting into a logical or predetermined structure of science policy. This pragmatic evolution is characteristic of the development of science and technology themselves and therefore, it seems to me, is proper for the accommodation of the rapidly changing nature of science. Indeed, I think I should add that the American political system is on the whole uniquely well adapted for dealing with science policy for the characteristic of science is its dynamic quality. The constantly changing relation between its parts and the growth of new parts of fields previously unimportant —the openness and pluralistic character of the federal system is, in my opinion, much better adapted to accommodating science than the more centralized parliamentary system of government with its tradition of rigid separation of means and ends, of techniques and purposes. This system has served us well. At the outbreak of World War II and again during the "Cold War," we have seen the quick response of American institutions and of the educational system that had brought higher education to a larger fraction of the population than in any other country, but without sacrificing excellence at the apex. Many concrete evidences point to the general strength of American science and technology. The importance of technical know-how as an item of export, our favorable balance of trade in patents, the high component of science-based products in our exports, the strength of our military technology, the overwhelming preponderance of citations of American scientific literature in European and Russian basic research journals, the percentage of Nobel prizes coming to Americans—all are sources of pride, though I hope not of complacency, since both Europe and the USSR, though behind, show signs of rapidly catching up.

And now I should like to mention the evolution of the present executive structure for science policy. As I stressed before, we began with a system that emphasized agency responsibility, and agencies were the primary instruments of science planning within the over-all fiscal ceilings set by general economic and political considerations and adjudicated by the Bureau of the Budget, with the right of agency appeal to the President. By political considerations, I mean, of course, the views of the Congress and the public as expressed directly and as evidenced through actions of the Congressional appropriations committees on previous budgets. A number of factors have increasingly made some form of coordination at the Presidential level inevitable. First and most obvious is the sheer magnitude of research and development activity, now grown to more than 15 percent of the administrative budget and sometimes estimated at 35 percent or more of the disposable part of the administrative budget. Nearly 60 percent of all federal employees at the professional level are scientists, engineers, or health personnel.

Second, the creation of agencies whose missions are defined in terms of means rather than ends, especially the Atomic Energy Commission (AEC), the National Aeronautics and Space Administration (NASA), and, to a lesser extent, the National Science Foundation, have created or generated problems of coordination. Each of these agencies is characterized by the fact that it serves several different political purposes. For example, the AEC is concerned with nuclear weapons; it is concerned with the development of civilian nuclear power; it is concerned with the development of the use of isotopes. For NASA manned space flight is the primary mission by itself—a political mission if you will—but the agency is also concerned in weather, communications, solar system astronomy, and a large component of the basic research. This arrangement in which certain agencies are organized around means rather than political purposes has both advantages and disadvantages. In the early days of atomic energy, for example, it was almost inevitable that a technology that was so new and was understood by so few people had to be cultivated in a kind of hothouse, in order that it should have any viability at all within the federal structure. But, as it grows, it runs the risk of becoming an end in itself rather than a means of serving the purposes, the political purposes, set forth by the Congress and the Executive.

For this reason one often sees pressures from various quarters to set up new agencies again defined by means rather than ends, agencies such as the oceanography agency, for example, or an independent agency for weather modification.

Third, the increasing interdependence among areas of science and technology is a very important influence on organization. It used to be that a scientific discipline could be uniquely associated with a mission. The classical example of this is agriculture. By and large in the early days the sciences underlying agriculture could be more or less uniquely associated with agriculture. Contrast this with the situation of the space agency, which utilizes practically every branch of science that man cultivates, from biology and psychology to the physical sciences. Now, specialization from a mission viewpoint is only possible at the development end of the spectrum. The characteristic of modern science is that everybody's business is somewhat relevant to everybody else's. And this, of course, inevitably requires some sort of judgment or coordination mechanism that transcends the planning of individual agencies.

Fourth, the problem of interdependence becomes especially acute in the area of basic science and in the more fundamental aspects of applied science. It has been pointed out that basic science was called basic science just by virtue of the fact that the purposes for which it was undertaken were not clear at the time it was undertaken. Almost every time we are faced with a major national problem involving science we wish we had done more basic research in the past. Too often we are forced to substitute vastly expensive empirical testing for the systematic rational application of the basic scientific knowledge that we do not have. When we cannot predict, we must test. There is nothing left to do. I do not deny that empirical testing is a necessary part of every engineering development, but much of it could be saved by adequate knowledge in advance. One can easily list a number of current examples. When the question of negotiations for a nuclear test-ban treaty came to the fore, we discovered that our knowledge of seismology was a serious limiting factor in our ability to predict the performance of detection systems. Again, we suddenly find ourselves faced with the problem of contamination of the environment by pesticides, yet with so little basic knowledge existing that in fact we can hardly tell how serious the problem is, let alone do very much about it. Problems of nuclear weapons effects and missile defense depend on basic knowledge in atmospheric physics and atomic physics— fields of basic research that have been so neglected in the past that we find ourselves seriously inhibited in predicting the performance of such systems by lack of such knowledge, while at the same time national necessity forces us to conduct extensive full-scale tests, some of which might have been avoided had we adequately cultivated the basic underlying knowledge in the past.

All of these cases illustrate areas where prior neglect of basic research or exploratory applied research forced us to mount expensive crash programs.

Fifth is the problem, referred to in Congressman Roush's paper, of the impact of federal scientific activities on nongovernmental institutions and on the national economy. We must not only solve our current problems but preserve and strengthen our human and institutional resources for the future. The optimum distribution or allocation of resources from the standpoint of efficiency in dealing with our current problems may not produce exactly the same result as the optimum distribution of our resources from the standpoint of our future scientific strength, and thus geographical and institutional distribution become important issues. While it is easy to overexaggerate the influence of federal actions on the present distribution of research resources, federal responsibility is only partial, but it is still very vital. Clearly, in a system of support from many different agencies and institutions, some kind of coordination and some kind of over-all national policy guidance is necessary.

Sixth, we see to an increasing degree the appearance of technical missions which transcend the mission interests of any one federal agency. A good example to which I have already referred is basic research and, in fact, we see in 1965 for the first time in the President's budget a specific reference to the need for growth in our basic research strength independent of development programs for the national defense. There are other areas, such as oceanography and atmospheric sciences or materials, in which national interest in a very real sense transcends the particular interest of individual agencies. We have the problem, one of the most serious problems facing the Executive Branch, of how to deal with such government-wide programs. We face the alternative of creating entirely new agencies, as we did in the case of the AEC and NASA, or of creating a national program that is shared and coordinated among many individual agencies. The question is one between a single technique or subject of study serving many different purposes as in AEC and NASA versus many different purposes as imbedded in agencies utilizing the same technique and sharing some of the same facilities. The question of which is more important at the moment, the technique or the separate purposes, determines which route we take. It is my own belief that in the long run it is better to follow the route of multi-agency support rather than the route of creating new agencies. Yet in all fairness I must say that it remains to be demonstrated, that the route of multi-agency support can really be successful.

Now I should like to make some comments about the mechanisms that have evolved in recent years in response to the needs and requirements that I have just outlined. The principal Executive Branch instrument of science policy lies in the complex that consists of the Office of Science and Technology, the President's Science Advisory Committee, and the Federal Council for Science and Technology, plus a number of other coordinating agencies in the Executive Branch such as the Space Council. Within the framework of the executive office, the various mechanisms—the strands—are pulled together in the person of the multi-hatted Special Assistant to the President for Science and Technology. The Federal Council for Science and Technology directly represents the federal agencies and the problems and perspective of federal science administrators at the sub-cabinet level. The President's Science Advisory Committee provides a mechanism for utilizing the services of the outside scientific community, the nongovernmental scientific community, in the determination of federal science policy, primarily, however, in the area of what I should like to call "science for policy" rather than in the area of "policy for science." The Office of Science and Technology provides the permanent full-time staff which serves the interests and needs both of the Federal Council and the President's Science Advisory Committee and which is the primary instrument for dealing with the area that I should like to call Policy for Science. In this latter role, of course, it works very closely with the National Science Foundation, which has a national responsibility in this area, particularly in the area of basic research, and also serves as advisor to the Bureau of the Budget in its over-all function of adjudicating among the various demands for funds from the federal agencies.

Another important channel of advice and help from the outside scientific community, which is more specifically oriented toward representation of the scientific community, is the National Academy of Sciences and its very important sister organization, the National Research Council. It is hoped that this important channel is about to be augmented by the new engineering academy, which will bring into the councils of government more representation and help from the engineering community. It is important to remember in this connection, however, that already the National Research Council has, to a large extent, served as a vehicle for the use and representation of the engineering community, but largely with respect to specific governmental problems rather than with respect to broad national policy. The point that I should like to emphasize is that the mechanism that I have described is an evolutionary one and one that is still rather rapidly evolving. There have been complaints about this mechanism, which, interestingly enough, seemed to polarize in two directions. On the one hand, there are complaints that it has been too powerful, too effective; on the other hand, there are complaints that it has been too weak, and too ineffective. Particular complaint has been directed against the ubiquitous role of the Special Assistant, the fact that he is at the same time director of the Office of Science and Technology, Special Assistant to the President for Science and Technology, chairman of the Federal Council, and chairman of the President's Science Advisory Committee. But, in my opinion at least, this multi-hatted role is essential to the effective operation of science advice in the executive branch. It does not mean necessarily that all scientific advice is given by one man. In fact, the scientific advisors of the various federal agencies also have a channel to the President. Furthermore, and I think this is the most important point, the long-range effectiveness of any scientific advisor in the government depends on the ability of the advisory mechanism to deal effectively with the short-range problems as well as long-range problems. Too often I have seen very eloquent and effective reports completely ignored because they came from a group which was not really "plugged in" on the day-to-day problems of executive decision-making. Yet the same recommendation and the same reports made by a group or by an individual that was deeply imbedded in the short-range decision-making process—in putting out fires, if you will—will be listened to very much more attentively. Looking at the weaknesses of the present structure, I think one can say that it has been highly effective for incremental and evolutionary changes in the system that exists. It has not so clearly been effective in making larger changes to the extent that these may be desirable. For example, by and large, it has not been able to alter the missions of the agencies, or rather I should say to secure the alteration of missions of agencies, except in very exceptional cases, such as the transformation of National Advisory Committee for Aeronautics into NASA under the emergency conditions following Sputnik. It has been largely unsuccessful in enlarging an agency's own concept of its mission responsibilities. By and large, it has a limited capability to plan. I know that the term planning frightens most scientists as it does me. Nevertheless, I think that this is partly based on a misunderstanding, because, when the word planning is mentioned, it is very often conceived in Marxian terms, the kind of monolithic planning of everything in detail that is characteristic of the Soviet structure. But planning, I think, rightly conceived, is not central direction but is rather a system for illuminating choices. In my opinion, the task of the Executive Branch is to develop realistic alternatives that the public and the Congress can understand. I think it is true that the cardinal choices in science and technology are essentially political choices. Whether we put our emphasis on space, whether we put it on health, whether we put it on a poverty program, and so on, are political questions, and, once we have chosen the directions of emphasis, the scientific choices follow, to some extent at least, from these political choices, the more so, of course, the more we are talking about the applied end of the spectrum. It seems to me that, when Congress is not presented with such alternatives and the alternative consequences of the various choices are not clearly spelled out, it has a tendency to occupy itself with "nuts and bolts," which are better left to administrative decision, or to occupy itself with parochial rather than global issues.

William Harris

IMPACT OF PROFESSIONAL SOCIETIES

My discussion relates to engineering societies and their role in national science policy. The voice of engineering in these matters has not been heard even though the engineering profession now comprises some 800,000 people in this country and a hundred or more societies that attempt to provide a means for engineers to communicate. Of these hundred organizations, twenty-three are important national institutions with 650,000 members. The function of these societies in the field of engineering has been primarily that of disseminating information on new technology through technical meetings and publications. But the engineering profession is restive at the present time, not at all convinced that the role it has played through these societies is responsive to the current issues. If the professional societies do provide a forum for the discussion of new technology and for new research discoveries, why is it that in these forums there has not been full discussion of national science policy issues? I think the answer is unfortunately clear. In large part, there has not been significant national research on these problems. Furthermore, there has not been a sense of need in these societies for an accounting of progress in dealing with these issues. I should like to describe some of the issues that the societies are beginning to become aware of in order to indicate how existing societies, intersociety groups, and new institutions in the profession are attempting to play a different role.

The first of these issues has to do with a broad field of materials, the second has to do with the Appalachian problems, and the third with the broad problem of oceanography and ocean engineering.

In the field of minerals and materials, there has been an enormous demand in the United States in the last two decades to move rapidly ahead toward making available to designers a whole range of materials that were curiosities when I was in school at Purdue University twenty-five years ago. At least fifteen metallic elements are now available for engineering application that were only used as chemical curiosities up to 1940. And all of these materials have come about as a result of federal support of research and development to meet the needs of the national defense program. At the same time, we have been relatively content to allow the pace of development of processes for the mining of these materials and for their extraction to move at the rate dictated by the needs of the civilian economy. This is not necessarily a bad thing, but it has had a number of interesting consequences. When I visited one of the largest copper mines and smelters in the country in 1965, I found that the processes and the pieces of equipment that were in use, aside from the materials handling equipment, were identical with those that I learned about at Purdue University twenty-five years earlier.

This disparity in rate of development is of growing concern to the engineering profession. The American Institute of Mining, Metallurgical and Petroleum Engineers (AIME) is attempting to determine whether the rate of technological advance in extractive and process metallurgy and in mining technology is rapid enough to be responsive to the changing pattern of national requirements. The institution in the federal government concerned with this field, the United States Bureau of Mines, does not have contract authority. It cannot contract with institutions such as Purdue University for research in the same way the Defense Department, National Aeronautics and Space Administration, and the Atomic Energy Commission can and do contract. Accordingly, the link between educational institutions and that agency of the federal government is incomplete and inadequate. The profession is faced by the fact that one essential technical field is fading away. As an inspector of engineering departments across the country, I have found that many universities are dropping the option in mining and in extractive metallurgy but, at the same time, very substantially expanding work in material science. This pattern is responsive to programs that in turn are responsive to present national goals and objectives. AIME has an opportunity now to examine whether the imbalance that has resulted from federal programs of the last two decades should continue. If the AIME does not make this examination, the problem will not be examined; this role for the profession is only now being recognized. The profession is defining the approaches that it can make to this problem and the ways that its findings can receive public attention.

The second general issue that I would like to describe relates to Appalachia. The federal government has committed over $1 billion to attempt to bring to Appalachia the benefits of modern society. The engineering profession has not been involved in any important manner in the planning or the analysis of utilization of these funds. This comment is not meant to be critical. The economists, the behavioral scientists, and the political figures in the country have identified the Appalachian problems and have taken steps to try to cope with them, but the engineering profession has not marshaled its resources or addressed its attention to what technology can contribute to Appalachia.

Let me be a little more specific. A third of the economy of West Virginia derives from coal mining. Four thousand miles of streams in West Virginia are polluted by acid mine wastes. Coal mining is going to continue, more streams are going to be polluted in the present pattern of development. Question: Is there a technology or a series of technologies that can cope with the pollution from coal mines? If these exist, how will they affect the economic factors of coal mining? Will they drive coal off the market if they are applied?

Another very proper and important technological issue that we have an opportunity to give attention to is the construction of roads in Appalachia for which $600 million is now committed. The construction of roads per se would obviously mean construction jobs, but studies made of the economic impact of a road system on a region suggest that it may be hundreds of miles long but only two or three miles transverse to the road itself. These studies suggest that all the facilities in a modern highway system that derives income from the tourists and others using the road are placed there not by local institutions—local with respect to the road itself—but by institutions five hundred miles along the road. Some of the issues relating technology to that road system that have not yet been examined or explored are: the problem of determining what has to be done in terms of transportation engineering; what can be done in terms of marshaling local resources so as to relate these opportunities for utilizing the road system to advance the economic development of West Virginia; how can the educational institutions be linked to these problems so that the local population can develop the competence to manage, run and operate these facilities; what should be done in land-use planning to provide at highway interchanges the facilities to process goods and repackage them in transit. In order to assure that attention is given to these problems, one of the intersociety groups, the Engineering Foundation, is co-sponsoring with the West Virginia University a study of more effective application of technology to the problems of Appalachia.

Let us now consider the third issue. In the early part of 1965 the Geneva convention on the continental shelf was signed. This convention provides that the boundary of the United States and of all other countries bordering the ocean extends along the ocean floor to that point at which the ocean reaches a depth of 200 meters. According to this convention, we own the resources on the bottom that are contiguous to shores to that depth of water. We are not permitted to exploit these in a way that would interfere with the freedom of transit of the seas above. We cannot introduce equipment that would interfere with the normal channels of commerce, but we do have ownership of the ocean bottom. The Geneva convention also provides that we can extend our boundaries to greater depths as our technological capability increases. Technology is the limiting factor in determining the ultimate boundaries of the United States. Present federal programs on oceanography derive almost entirely from the interest expressed by the scientific community. Since the late 1950s this community has been examining the need to understand the ocean. Through panels it has directed attention toward the importance of learning about the ocean. It has made cost-benefit analyses on what it would mean to the country to learn more about the ocean.

As a result of this dedicated effort, the 1966 federal budget provides for an oceanography program amounting to $150 million. But the ocean engineering component of that program is small. In order to exploit the opportunities established by the continental shelf, engineering progress must be made more rapidly than heretofore has been the case. It is necessary that the engineering profession encourage rapid progress in ocean engineering, not to compete with the $150 million allocated to research, but to support additional projects that will advance the national goal of expanded boundaries. The institution necessary for achieving this cannot be any one of the existing societies. It cannot be an intersociety grouping because these tend to be modest in scope. It was in anticipation of problems of this kind that the Engineers Joint Council began its move toward the establishment of a National Academy of Engineering in concert with the National Academy of Sciences. Organized under the aegis of the Academy, the new National Academy of Engineering can examine new national objectives, such as the deep ocean problem, consider these in harmony with the interests of the science programs and work toward the development of a consensus as to the comprehensive national program of ocean science and ocean engineering.

Professional societies can engage in further studies of the kind that I have discussed. However, unless I misunderstand the tenor of discussions in the profession, the societies are acting as though they believe that with a National Academy of Engineering, the individual societies can relax because there has been created an institution that can provide leadership for engineering in the national interest. It has been my experience that for too long we have made it necessary for a few people to carry the full burden of discussion, analysis, and debate of these matters. I am sure that some of them are getting tired. It is too much to ask that one man, or twenty men, or a few hundred, in the National Academies of Sciences and Engineering and in the special groups such as the President's Science Advisory Committee carry the national burden of debate and discussion in these fields. If a democratic society is going to function maturely, thousands of people should be involved because thousands of people contribute to the translation of these policies into programs. These thousands of people that are in our professional societies, whether in science or engineering, are the constituency. They are the individuals in the country that can convey to their Congressmen and to their universities their views as to the desirable posture of the country in technology. It is not enough to create a few new institutions to provide an opportunity for a few people to assume positions of leadership. If science policy, engineering policy, and public policy are going to be related to each other in a meaningful and significant sense, I believe it inevitable, that the engineering societies are going to have to be very deeply involved in discussions of these policies.

These societies came to maturity long before federal programs had their present impact on national developments. They came to maturity before World War II, but the issues we are talking about here became important after World War II. The societies have a tax-exempt status that leads their treasurers and some members of their boards of directors to fear involvement with affairs in Washington because of a possible loss of tax exemption. I do not favor the loss of tax-exempt status. I recognize that many activities relating to the federal government do not involve lobbying. Much can be done without urging a Congressman to take a position favorable to the field of engineering, that is, to lobby. In striving to create an effective forum for the debate of these issues, we can take a leaf from the book of some of our European counterparts.

For example, in Norway, they faced a major national problem: Who should own the hydroelectric sites not yet developed in Norway? The engineering professions came together and said: "We can lay out the technological problems. If we can bring into focus the political, economic, and business views, we can arrive at a national consensus." And so they did.

As Sir Eric Ashby stated in his paper, in Germany the professional societies are debating the issue of how much support the German government should give to research—an issue that none of our professional societies, to the best of my knowledge, has tried to debate in this country.

In *Harper's Magazine,* about 1950, there was the account of a man who had moved from the center of the city to the country in search of peace and quiet. He found it—for one week. Then his neighbors called on him. He was delighted to see them because they were congenial. When they suggested that he might join with them in certain activities, he said that he would be delighted; he had lots of free time now. After three months, according to the story, he found that he was involved three nights a month in PTA meetings. Another three months passed, and he was engaged about two nights a week in discussions of local financing, housing, and education. Finally he wrote an account of his experiences under the title "Whom Shall We Picket Tonight?"

All of you know the degree to which a professional society can call on your time even with its current function as a forum for the discussion of new science and technology and as a publisher of technical journals. If these societies are to create a forum for the discussion of national issues, it will be necessary to have a very substantial involvement from individuals in the engineering professions. The opportunity is very real. Professional societies are gradually coming to understand this. If the universities will begin to develop an awareness on the part of their students as to these national problems and to make such discussions an integral element of their engineering schools, we will find that the professional societies of the next decade will make increasingly important contributions to the national consensus on national science and technological policy problems.

Albert V. Crewe

SCIENCE ON A REGIONAL SCALE

Before beginning this discussion of some of the regional aspects of scientific endeavors, I think it is extremely important to establish one simple concept, and that is the enormous scope of modern science. There is almost no field of human endeavor that has not been in some way or another affected and even transformed by modern science. We are intimately aware of many of these invasions. We are conscious of the impact of the computer on banking systems, accounting systems, and inventory control. We are informed every day of the superb efforts that are being made by those involved in the space program. We have felt the impact of modern science in communication, in entertainment, and in our everyday conveniences. A little thought will also demonstrate the effect of modern science even on our cultural life. Computers have written music and poetry, and the revolution in materials has had visible effects on the plastic and decorative arts.

One must add to this concept of an all-encompassing activity the fact that scientific knowledge is expanding at an ever-increasing pace. There is something in the mind of man that makes him demand explanations. In some people this desire to understand is an overwhelming force. In this era the people possessing this are called scientists, and, owing to their efforts and success, our knowledge of the world in which we live is increasing every day. What was a daydream yesterday becomes a possibility today and a fact tomorrow.

We often confuse these two principal aspects of science: the search for and acquisition of knowledge, on the one hand, and its application for practical purposes, on the other. For the moment, I should like to draw a distinction. Having made this distinction, we can establish the thesis that scientific applications of science that are already widespread will become ever more encompassing. This thesis could hardly be disputed, and it is perhaps wise for all of us to accept it rather than to fight it. As a consequence of this thesis, we must all recognize that, if we do not now have the knowledge to solve a particular problem, then soon—perhaps very soon—we *shall* possess that knowledge, and, moreover, if there is an area into which the scientific method has not yet been applied, it may only be a matter of time before it *is* so applied. There are indeed many areas of our lives in which science and technology have barely entered, but we should all be aware that this state of affairs is only temporary and may only be this way because of a lack of demand for knowledge on the part of the nonscientist or a lack of understanding and interest on the part of the scientist. In time, these intellectual and psychological barriers will come down.

On a national or federal scale science has had a number of great successes and has been encouraged and applied in almost every conceivable area. Science and technology have become national tools to be applied to such things as atomic power, the exploration of space, the defense of our country, the exploitation of its natural resources, and the defense of the dollar. It is hardly necessary to justify my claim of success because our newspapers are filled almost every day with events in support of this statement. Because of its enormous success, the federal government supports scientific research through its many agencies with a sizable fraction of the federal budget.

There is a strong justification for considering regional aspects of modern science and technology. These regional needs arise from a variety of sources, and in any one region they arise in particular from its natural assets or deficiencies, in the cultural climate or lack of it, and the degree of industrial development or lack of it. These qualities occur in an infinite variety of combinations, but, because of the historical development of the population and the geographical quality of an area, they naturally group into fairly well-defined regions.

Bearing in mind our original thesis, we should now ask what form or shape scientific contributions should take for a particular region. In this respect, we can focus our attention on two principal areas, namely, the search for knowledge and also its application.

If we focus our attention first on the acquisition of knowledge, we shall find, of course, that a large proportion of this takes place within the universities. For the past hundred years or so the universities have been the location for basic research. This has not always been so, nor need it remain so. There is, however, an undeniable strong and close link between the basic research scientist and education. The link, of course, is through the organizations that conduct basic research and participate in the race for knowledge, and these are the large, multi-disciplinary, federally supported laboratories. They arose as a national need for the acquisition of specific kinds of knowledge, in particular that related to the development of nuclear energy. They have now become regional laboratories containing staff and facilities little different from those of major universities in the same region. This transformation has taken place gradually, casually, and without the blessing of a preconceived plan of development. Yet they are here, and they are indispensable. The problem of today is how to integrate the university community and these laboratories.

In the Midwest we are attempting such an integration and are convinced that it will succeed. The driving force for this move came from a quarter that is at the same time unusual and a typical product of the modern scientific age. This is the increasing difficulty and cost of performing experiments at the forefront of science. As time goes by, the experimental equipment that is required for these investigations becomes extremely large and extremely expensive. Because of their size, because of their cost, and because they are indeed at the forefront of modern science, these devices become the focal point for great scientific activity. I am specifically referring to the large particle accelerators that have been aptly termed "the cathedrals of modern science." Again, because of their size and their cost, they tend to be located at the center, or close to the center, of some large circle of academic activity and therefore enter into the general domain of regional science.

These accelerators were located in the federally supported laboratories because the laboratories were already large and already operating and constructing large experimental equipment. It is, therefore, inevitable for the large laboratories and the universities to act in close concert if the total program is to be a success.

Specifically, our problem at Argonne National Laboratory arose with the completion and the successful operation of our own large accelerator. This accelerator had been designed for the use of the whole community of Midwest research scientists. It was located, however, in a laboratory owned by the Atomic Energy Commission and operated under contract to the Commission by one single educational institution—the University of Chicago. This situation proved to be an impossible conflict. It was a natural desire of Midwestern scientists to have control over their own destinies. This is entirely understandable because in this area of research there is but one laboratory for any region, and for the scientists within that region this particular facility represents their only source of experimental material. Therefore, to have a situation where this source was controlled by one institution was, to many people, intolerable. The solution that we have found is to arrange a three-way contrast between the Atomic Energy Commission, the University of Chicago, and a new corporation composed of those institutions interested in the work of the Laboratory. The new corporation will be responsible for the formation, approval, and review of all the Laboratory's policies, while the University of Chicago will still assume the responsibility of operating the Laboratory in a manner responsive to the desires and decisions of the corporation. It is hoped in this way to take advantage of the wisdom and knowledge of the whole community of scientists for the conduct of the Laboratory and at the same time to be able to take advantage of the experience and skill of the University of Chicago in managing such a large operation as the Laboratory—a task that the University has performed so well for almost twenty years.

We are sure that this arrangement will succeed, but we have not had a chance as yet to try it.

This management problem specifically arose because of one particular piece of experimental equipment, namely, our large synchrotron. The remedy, however, has been applied to the total Laboratory. The reason for this is that it soon became apparent to those who were deliberating on this problem that the accelerator was only a symptom or a symbol of things to come, that the natural tendency is for research equipment to get larger and more expensive as the problems become more complicated and the solutions more sophisticated. This being so, it is almost certainly true that a similar problem may very well arise in the future with respect to other pieces of research equipment. The remedy was therefore applied to the whole Laboratory management structure.

We in the Midwest are entering into a new era of necessary cooperation. We have little doubt that the road will not be smooth—at least during the transition period. We do believe, however, that we are pioneering in a kind of operation that might prove to be a model for future facilities of a similar character. If we succeed, the way is open for other multi-institution facilities to receive the same kind of combination of skills and wisdom. One can conceive, for example, that future large accelerators could benefit from a similar structure, that such things as giant computer centers or medical computers operating diagnostic centers could be operated in a similar manner.

This example is just one of the ways in which one region of this country is assembling its varied and various forces for the mutual benefit of all concerned. In the last few years this kind of cooperative activity has been growing and, indeed, even proliferating. There is little doubt that future years will see much more of this kind of multi-institutional research effort.

It should be clear that we have not, by any means, found the ultimate answer to our organizational problems. A look into the future should serve to convince anyone of this fact. Universities are growing larger, and more of them are moving into more areas of graduate education. The number and scope of other laboratories is also growing, and many of these should logically be controlled by universities. If, in every case, one must protect the interests of the faculty by insisting on a "multi-university" management, we face the ultimate prospect of every university being a part of the management of every laboratory. Such a solution is obviously ludicrous.

Perhaps a better solution would be for the laboratories to have simpler management but for all operators of laboratories to be members of a National Convention that could establish and enforce the ethics of such laboratory management.

What has just been described is typical of the kind of activity that is taking place in the area of most concern to the academic and basic research community. There are, however, many problems that are not clearly university problems but are, nevertheless, regional and scientific and urgent. The solution of these problems is less well defined because in many cases there is no existing structure upon whose foundations the new organizations can grow.

We might take, for example, the case of water pollution. This is obviously a regional problem because our problems here in the Midwest with the proximity of the Great Lakes are undeniably different from those on the West Coast or the East Coast. This problem has received a great deal of attention in the last few months, but it will obviously be some time before mechanisms for solutions of these problems are established. The problem is obviously a scientific one because modern science and technology can be applied to its solution.

Another example would be that of air pollution, which so far has received less attention. With the growing density in population these pollution problems will eventually become so pressing as to demand immediate solution. We must attempt to solve these problems before the demand is immediate so that we may arrive at a logical, economic, and simple solution.

There is little doubt that as the population density increases that the ultimate solution to these two problems is for property owners, be they industrial or domestic, to ensure that any liquid or gaseous effluent that emerges from the boundary of their property must be either potable or breathable or disposed of in community sewers where it can be made potable or breathable. This is the ultimate solution to the problem, and science can be used to provide the technological answer. This same criterion must eventually be applied even to community sewage disposal. There can be little doubt that ultimately even a sewage plant will find it necessary to provide potable water as its effluent. Such a solution is certainly feasible today by using the same kind of technique that has been proposed for the desalination of sea water. It is not clear, however, whether such a solution is economical. Ultimately, such a solution must become economical because it will be necessary. Surely today we should move in this general direction before it is too late.

There are other regional problems to which science and technology could be applied but that so far have not received adequate attention. I shall mention two of these, namely, that of transportation and that of crime.

Transportation problems are to a great extent local. The problem of moving people and goods is different in Chicago than, say, San Francisco or New York. It is only within comparatively recent history that scientific methods have been used for the analysis and control of traffic. It may be some time before science and technology are fully applied to the solution of transportation problems. It must eventually happen.

In the case of crime, this is a problem that is a growing one and that again is certainly local, for the pattern of crime depends upon geography and so does its solution. We have not as a nation applied scientific methods to the control and prevention of crime. There are very few crime laboratories within the country. These laboratories in total are not sufficient to cope with the problem. Crime laboratories so far have been used principally for detection methods and for filing systems as, for example, for fingerprints. It is conceivable, however, that modern science could equally well be applied to the prevention of crime and that, if enough investment were made, we might very well make great inroads into the two problems of crime detection and crime prevention.

There are undoubtedly many other regional problems that would be susceptible to the application of science and technology. We must be continually on the lookout for these problems before they reach such a magnitude that nothing will help.

On the industrial level there are also regional problems that could be subjected to scientific method.

Many years ago a determined effort was made to raise the level of this country's agricultural system, and an excellent organization was devised for this purpose. A link was provided between agricultural research establishments and stations and the farmers. The link provided was a personal one, and the net result is one that we are all aware of and that is the envy of the rest of the world. We now have the most efficient and the most productive agricultural system that has ever existed. It is perhaps somewhat surprising that no one has used this excellent example as a possible model for modern industrial development. We rely heavily at the moment upon the individual initiative of an industrial company to provide its own information from its own research and development organization, and yet we are certain that this cannot work. With the exception of the largest industrial organizations, no industrial company can afford to provide its own knowledge. On the other hand, knowledge is being developed through the federal laboratories and through the university laboratories that could, in principle, be applied to the solution of industrial problems and the provision of new industrial techniques. Yet, as time goes by, the industrial community and the research community must inevitably draw farther apart. As knowledge expands and research laboratories become more involved in this search for knowledge, then their techniques become more sophisticated, their language becomes more unintelligible, and the ultimate wisdom is produced in a form that is not readily digestible by the lay public.

We are therefore creating a gap between those who are producing the knowledge and those who need it. The written word is not enough to bridge this gap. The number of technical publications is already beyond the scope of even the specialist. It would be unthinkable for a small company to hope to keep abreast of modern developments of all the fields of science that could possibly have an impact upon its business. We could, in principle, take the example of the agricultural development and provide the same kind of extension service on a personal basis, and I am quite convinced that this would have enormous benefits.

In conclusion, then, the potential power of modern science and technology is enormous. We can predict with certainty an ever-expanding knowledge and an ever-widening sphere of application of this knowledge. Much of this work will perforce be on a national scale either because of cost or because problems to be solved are specifically national. Much, however, can be done and must be done on a regional scale. Many of the problems are necessarily regional because of geography or because of history. We do appear to have adequate systems for the solution of national problems, but on a regional basis we are only beginning to be aware of the potential. Being aware, however, is the first step toward a solution.

Philip H. Abelson

MIDWESTERN INSTITUTIONS AND
THE SCIENTIFIC REVOLUTION

Science and technology are increasingly shaping our society and its economy. Those who understand the power of the new tools and use them wisely will prosper and grow. Laggards in facing the new realities will experience economic stagnation. The Middle West has begun to wonder whether it has fully met the challenges of the Scientific Revolution. But there is a ferment in the air that suggests that change may be imminent.

In a recent speech at the Midwestern Governors' Conference, Charles Kimball, President of the Midwest Research Institute, outlined some of their current problems. His institute had made a study of a six-state region, including Iowa, Kansas, Missouri, and Nebraska. During the decade 1950–60 the number of jobs in the area had increased only 2.3 percent against 14.5 percent for the nation. The average family income is now much below the national figure and is still going down. During the period more than a million people moved to other parts of the country. Although there was a slight total population increase, it was much less than the national average. Kimball pointed out that the brain drain from the Middle West is very large indeed. For instance, Iowa colleges and universities awarded 72,000 degrees from 1950 to 1960, and yet the number of college graduates living in Iowa increased by only 19,000 during the period. The two state universities estimate that 55–75 percent of the graduates leave the state for their first jobs. I might add that only a small percentage of Purdue's PH.D.s find jobs in Indiana.

Kimball emphasized this loss of talent by saying:

In the adequate and appropriate use of its human resources, the Midwest is not doing well. We have been losing our good people at an alarming rate, and not attracting their replacements. Yet the Midwest grows and educates a disproportionately high percentage of the best minds in the country, not just scientists, but intellectually capable people in all fields. Many of these people leave here because they do not find challenging opportunities.

The Midwest has the assets and resources to compete with, and in fact to lead, other regions. It's in the profitable and self-satisfying employment of human talents and brainpower that this region has failed so far to live up to its potential. . . . This area is 15 years behind both coasts in its use of this type of resource.

If the trends outlined by Kimball were to continue, parts of the Middle West could become a national problem—a new kind of Appalachia. Today the region is prosperous, but prosperity is not guaranteed forever. Science and technology are creating new products that displace older ones, and new technology can render the greatest of industries obsolescent. Even industries that are world-known can lose their competitive position if they do not take the lead in creating and applying new technology. Consider the experience of the steel industry, in which the Midwest has an important role. In 1950 the competitive position of the United States was excellent. Our export price was substantially less than that of the Europeans. The fact that this country was a net exporter of steel contributed its share to a favorable balance of payments. By 1960 the situation was reversed. The Europeans had cut their costs while ours had increased. As a result the United States became an importer of steel, and billions of dollars have left this country to pay for steel imports. If our steel industry had remained competitive, we should not be nearly so concerned about the gold drain.

Other industries of the Middle West, such as consumer electronics, are facing increasingly tough international competition. This region must exert itself more imaginatively if it is not to become a drag on the nation's economy and our international status.

I have mentioned some of the symptoms of decay in parts of the Middle West. What is lacking in this region? What are features that characterize more vital areas of this country? I shall not pretend to supply all the answers to these questions; I doubt if anyone could. But let us consider the Boston area. From some standpoints the Northeast and the Middle West are fairly well matched. The climate of the two regions is about equally rigorous. New England has fewer natural resources. Educational facilities are comparable. Several of the institutions in the Midwest are about on a level with Harvard. The University of Illinois, for example, educates well and carries on fundamental research comparable in quality to that of Harvard. I believe that the universities of the Middle West are performing their educational functions well. A major difference in the two regions is in the effectiveness of the transfer of knowledge to those concerned with industrial applications. Innovators and entrepreneurs are abundant in Boston. Risk-taking capital is available. More of the wealthy persons have a sense of public responsibility.

The history of the development of xerography should be a source of chagrin and an object lesson to the Midwest. Xerography was invented by Chester Carlson, a patent attorney. The Battelle Memorial Institute in Ohio took over the invention and proceeded to develop it. When the process had been brought to the stage of being practically ready for commercial development, Battelle tried to interest local wealthy people in backing the project. At that time the investment needed was a mere $100,000. But Battelle could not find backers for the project in the Middle West. Eventually, Battelle transferred the development to the Haloid Company of Rochester, New York, for an equity position in the company. That company, now known as Xerox Corporation, has outstanding stock on the New York Stock Exchange valued at more than $2.5 billion. Middle Westerners fumbled a chance to make a tremendous fortune. They also lost, for the region, the advantage of having the exploiting company located there.

The Battelle Memorial Institute provides another lesson in the potential constructive role of private wealth. The institute was established by the will of Gordon Battelle, who in 1923 left money for "the encouragement of creative research . . . and the making of discoveries and inventions." All together, the Battelle family left the Institute $3.5 million. Today it is the leading institution of its kind anywhere. It has been a great contributor to the nation's strength both in war and in peace. It has assets of about $100 million. It em-

ploys some 5,000 people, many of whom are leaders in the application of science and technology to the nation's problems. It understands
how to gear science to society's needs. In the difficult years ahead,
Battelle will continue to provide leadership as we face increasingly
complex social and economic problems.

Recently I was delighted to visit another institution that is a great
credit to the Midwest—Linda Hall Library, in Kansas City, a science
library containing one of the best and most useful scientific collec-
tions in the country. It was established in 1947 by a bequest of $6
million by Herbert F. Hall. During the last eighteen years a great collection has been assembled and housed. Some 10,000 periodicals are
received. Through wise management the endowment has grown to
$23 million. The best feature of the library is its usefulness, for it is
probably the most nationally helpful establishment of its kind. When
scientists at Huntsville, Alabama, say, need an article published in an
obscure journal, their librarian wires an order to the Linda Hall Library. The same day, a copy of the material is dispatched. Only a
nominal fee is charged.

Common ingredients in these two situations are a wise benefactor,
a broad, flexible charter, a public-spirited board of trustees, and competent, imaginative leaders to implement the charters. Other contributions of public-spirited men to the Midwest could be cited, but the
record is not nearly so good as in other parts of the country. And why
has so small a part of the Ford billions been devoted to the Middle
West?

The Massachusetts Institute of Technology engaged in a drive to
raise $66 million; it obtained $98 million. Stanford University started
a five-year campaign to get $100 million; in half that time the fund
was oversubscribed.

The wealthy and powerful people of the Midwest are facing a new
challenge and opportunity. They could create the agencies to provide
leadership for the region. If they fail to take the initiative, the burden
will be assumed by politicians. For the next fifteen years the central
goal for the Midwest should be to do what is necessary to achieve the
intellectual and technological leadership of this country. It cannot be
obtained by political manipulation or by "me too" tactics. Political action could bring federal contracts to the Midwest, but they would

carry with them no guarantee of lasting stimulus to the economy. A recent study by Albert Shapero of the Stanford Research Institute showed that Department of Defense supported research and development in Denver, Tucson, and Orlando did not generate new associated enterprises.

"Me too" tactics are simply another way of guaranteeing mediocrity; they ensure that their proponents will do no better than hold the second-best hand. Many of the currently successful institutions, like Battelle, owe their position to courageous innovation. Their builders saw a need before others saw the opportunity. They were ahead of the times and in tune with them. If the Midwest is to assume leadership, it must gage the future accurately. It must evaluate special strengths and opportunities and exploit them. It must find new or more effective patterns for creative activity and more effective means of meshing the opportunities of science with the needs of society. These suggestions imply the utilization of long-range evaluation and planning groups. I believe such groups should be established. Under proper auspices, a nominal sum of money, wisely spent, could produce valuable guidance.

Suppose that an influential group of citizens contributed funds for such a study and that a blue-ribbon board of trustees was assembled. The trustees could act to appoint a director of the study groups. They could help in recruiting panelists from industry and elsewhere. The trustees could then serve as a group influential in the implementation of recommendations.

Achievement of leadership will not be easy. The Midwest must start from behind. Other regions, farther ahead, will also be active, and they will not stand still to allow competitors to pass them. I believe that the situation will require a continuing series of studies and actions for at least fifteen years. There is need also for good judgment in making present-day decisions, particularly in the area of political activity relating to the location of federal technical facilities. Capturing some installations would be worth a bruising battle and the expenditure of political capital. Others are not worth the effort. The contrast is exemplified by two recently under discussion.

One was an electronics research facility for the space agency. Electronics is a key to the future, and the kind of advanced technology involved in the National Aeronautics and Space Administration facility would be likely to have a substantial multiplier effect. It could lead to the creation of entirely new industries. If the Midwest had been on the ball, it would have united solidly on one location, and a carefully organized, unified drive might well have forced a favorable decision. Actually, far more effort was devoted to a less worthy cause—the fight to obtain the Midwest Universities Research Association accelerator. High-energy physics has produced almost no practical industrial benefits and few multiplier effects. It is clear to me that the Midwest's Congressional representatives need better guidance than they have been getting.

We often hear it said that no one can predict where science and technology will take us. I believe that such an attitude is defeatist and not well grounded. Surprises do occur, of course, but many long-term trends can be successfully extrapolated. It seems very likely that electronics, automation, and computers, already very important, will have even greater impact in the future. In the field of creative science the most notable advances will probably arise in molecular biology. We will come nearer to understanding living processes in all their phases, with resultant benefits in the treatment of disease. At the same time we will make marked progress in understanding the human mind; we may even learn how to make it function better. As a result of discoveries already made, and more to come, human life will be prolonged. This trend will be accompanied by two major effects. First, the time and energy devoted to education, both in youth and throughout life, will increase. Education will become an even greater industry than it is now. The second effect will be an expansion of the effort devoted to the care of the aged. Indeed, medical care will be one of the greatest growth industries.

These are a few major trends that can readily be seen. I feel confident that other important continuing developments could be identified. If one could obtain a well-conceived view of the future, planning would be more useful and feasible. Such planning would also take into account the potentials of various institutions in meeting future needs and opportunities. Organizations are crucial to meeting the complex problem of gearing science and technology to the needs of society. I shall mention three kinds of creative institutions that have important future roles.

In meeting future opportunities the Middle West has many assets. It is a prosperous region, with many fine universities and colleges. Most of its states have an exemplary record in supporting higher education. Indiana, for one, has a particularly good record. In terms of its population, Indiana devotes a very large sum of money to its universities and produces a splendid stream of PH.D.s.

One of the liabilities of the region is that most of its universities are situated in rural areas. A generation or two ago such a location was appropriate. Students were removed from the distractions of the big city. Moreover, much of the useful interaction of the university with society was through agriculture, which was highly important to the economy. Now, agriculture has been revolutionized, and only a relatively few farmers are required to produce our food. A university in a rural setting is handicapped in meeting today's technological challenges. The inconvenience of travel to and from such places acts as a major barrier to useful interactions. It is surely no accident that the major technological complexes elsewhere have been built around urban universities and that no major complex surrounds the more numerous rural institutions.

In seeking to meet the new competition in technology, politicians will be inclined to ask the universities to undertake additional functions. The universities enjoy excellent public esteem. When public funds are to be employed in a venture involving sciences, politicians turn to the universities. Indeed, the governor of a typical state could scarcely do otherwise. Were he not to call on the educational institutions of his state, he would appear to be showing a lack of confidence in them. Yet the times call for a different approach. The typical state university is at present facing tremendous problems of its own. Everywhere increasing numbers of students wish to be enrolled; facilities are strained; more buildings must be constructed; and more instructors must be hired. The typical university has now expanded to such an extent that it might well be called an educational factory. Moreover, its campus already houses a plethora of activities.

The great state universities are in the midst of an identity crisis.

They are trying to be all things to all people. It used to be said that a university president had to provide football for the alumni, parking for the faculty, and sex for the undergraduates. The role of the university has expanded beyond those requirements. But an organization that has many purposes cannot furnish the optimal environment for any one of them. The very size of the present-day institutions makes them inefficient in furnishing supporting services. Committees must function. Memoranda must be exchanged.

However, the universities could modify their policies in ways that would not interfere greatly with their educational functions—and might, indeed, strengthen them. They could, for example, establish branches especially for graduate study in science and engineering near metropolitan centers to permit easier and more fruitful interaction with industry. Another step leading to more interaction that could be taken immediately, would not be costly and could produce quick benefits would be to establish reciprocal sabbatical arrangements with industrial research organizations. New science would thus be efficiently transferred to industry, and an awareness of industrial problems would be brought to the university. As a result, training of engineers and applied scientists could be better geared to meet society's needs.

One way in which the Midwest could usefully pioneer would be to make a study of creativity and an investigation of how to achieve optimum creativity in an organization. I am convinced that most of our present research establishments are relatively inefficient.

A deeply ingrained attitude toward growth blinds us when we make decisions about size of institutions. Too often an increase in number is equated to progress. Too often men are judged not by the quality of their accomplishments but by the size of their team. One of the best investments the Middle West could make would be a careful study of the optimal size in relation to creative activity. I believe that such a study should also take a hard look at the advisability of concentrating more research activity at the large universities.

Just recently I was discussing this matter of optimum size with a man from a world-famous West Coast institution. Originally his organization had a staff of about forty. During the past two decades it had become ten times larger, and financial support had expanded even more. But this former director was sad and puzzled. He could not understand why its productivity had not increased correspondingly. The output, in fact, had only risen by a factor of three. My friend's remarks agree with my own impressions derived from visiting many installations. Very large research organizations have built-in inefficiencies that can reduce their effectiveness to as low as one third or one fifth that of the better-structured institutions.

Since optimum size for a research establishment is fundamental, I should like to dwell on the topic for a few moments. Let us approach the matter by considering an organization consisting of one research man and his supporting staff. I need not argue that this arrangement would be costly and inefficient and that usually the man would not be optimally creative. If a second scientist were added, and the two were congenial, they could interact very constructively. Overhead costs, like that of the library, would not rise very much, and the cost per person would go down. When the group was increased to four, further benefits of stimulus and economy would usually be achieved. But when the group became larger than four, added benefits per additional man would tend to diminish. Most creative scientists can have intense contact with only a limited number of others; too many contacts are frustrating and distracting. As the number in a group increases, the change of personality clashes also becomes greater.

In general, when the group is larger than six or seven, it can no longer function intimately as a group. Most of you have perhaps noted that in a gathering of more than seven people the conversation tends to break up into splinters; it cannot be held together unless there is a chairman and a conscious effort. As the group becomes larger, communication becomes even more difficult. Seminars must be arranged. And now, as the group expands, overhead increases with size. Administrative functionaries usurp a larger role. Interoffice memoranda multiply. Secretaries must be employed to type them and to answer the phones. In any large group there are certain to be "stinkers" whose conduct seems to require a set of rules and regulations. These individuals harass and annoy the just and the unjust alike. Then there comes to be a parking problem. There must be a spring dance. There must be much more formal machinery—a chain of command. Committees must be organized.

For the last twelve years I have been director of the Geophysical Laboratory of the Carnegie Institution of Washington. Our Laboratory is regarded by many as a world leader in the study of processes occurring in the earth. We have pioneered in work at very high pressures, in radioactive dating, in research on ore formation, and in organic geochemistry, to name a few fields. Visitors seeing the Laboratory for the first time express amazement that so much is accomplished by so few people. Our total staff amounts to only forty-five.

I think that, in comparison with many laboratories I have seen, we operate rather effectively. First, we have an agreed-on over-all broad objective—the study of the earth, employing physical-chemical methods. Within that framework we exploit new advances in technique, instrumentation, and theory to achieve new insights. We have one main goal: to gain knowledge and disseminate it. We have a steady flow of postdoctoral fellows, but the educational function does not interfere with our principal activity. The laboratory is free from distractions. A scientist, if he wishes, can work for days or even weeks without interruption. There are no committees. Only two memoranda are circulated each year. One sets forth the vacation schedule. The second asks the staff for material for our annual report. Only once a year is the group asked to give an accounting of its activities.

We operate on funds that come from an endowment, and only rarely do we use federal support. Accordingly, our budget, while adequate, is limited. Each member of the staff realizes this fact, and all cooperate in being careful about expenditures. Like scientists everywhere, all the staff would like to have the help of technicians. Yet we have none. The staff recognize that nonprofessional help costs almost as much per person as postdoctoral fellows, and they prefer that the funds be devoted to professional colleagues. They understand perhaps less clearly that technicians and personal secretaries are detrimental to creativity, for, while being helpful, they are a source of distraction.

We have an advantage not shared by most large organizations. When the case for action is clear, we can move fast. A decision to purchase can be made and an order placed in a few minutes.

Our Laboratory has all the facilities that a large organization could provide, including library and shop. In fact, these facilities are more accessible than they would be in a larger establishment. Our staff members have all the intellectual stimulus that they can usefully interact with. At the same time we are free of the distractions, committees, and nonproductive activity that are an inevitable part of a larger organization.

I shall conclude with a brief mention of a third kind of creative establishment. The Midwest is fortunate in having a number of nonprofit research organizations like the Battelle Memorial Institute, the Illinois Institute of Technology Research Institute, and the Midwest Research Institute. These organizations are staffed with highly competent men, accustomed to dealing with abstract science, on the one hand, and with hard-boiled industrialists, on the other. They are practiced in bridging the whole spectrum of the problem of utilizing science in the service of society. They are engaged in a highly competitive activity in which only the disciplined, imaginative, and sharp-witted can survive. They must constantly strive to be in tune with the future. They are a rich potential source of the kind of judgment that this region must employ if it is to make a bid for leadership.

I have called attention to parts of a very large set of problems. I do not know all the answers. But, I feel certain that the Midwest can and should do a better job than it has been doing. It is now beginning to move. If it is to move wisely and successfully, it must mobilize all its resources of money, of influential leading citizens, and of brain power. The potential of a great future is here. Will the challenges be adequately met?

Edward Teller

EDUCATION OF THE MODERN INVENTOR

One of my favorite books more than half a century ago was Jules Verne's *From the Earth to the Moon*. This book (which, apart from being very amusing and stimulating, is full of mistakes and which can be used to great advantage in the instruction of students by asking them to make a list of the mistakes) makes the prediction that the first firing in a space enterprise would be carried out by the "crazy" Americans. We all know that instead the "crazy" Russians have beat us to the punch. To my mind this is extremely significant, and not because space research has so great an importance, though it is indeed important. I think the main reason why some of us are worried is that Sputnik demonstrates a new situation that a few people begin to be aware of but that has not as yet penetrated into the general consciousness.

In the beginning of this century the United States was rather weak in pure science. On the other hand, there was no question that the United States was the leader in the application of the scientific results to industry. The United States was the home of Edison and of many other inventors who made the greatest possible contribution not only to the future of this country but to the development of the latest phase of the Industrial Revolution—a phase in which new, often surprising, scientific results were put to practical use.

The situation that prevailed at the beginning of the century has, in fact, been turned upside down. Today the United States is the unquestionable leader in pure science. At the same time, we have neglected application and are neglecting it to an increasing extent. In that field, I assert, the Russians have already surpassed us.

Science in the United States is greatly influenced by fashion. At one time in one discipline practically everybody who is anybody wants to work on the same limited field. In the 1920s it was spectroscopy; then suddenly spectroscopy became unfashionable. The change took place almost as rapidly as changes do take place in the fashion of ladies' hats. In the 1930s, instead of spectroscopy, our main attention was directed toward nuclear physics. In the 1930s nuclear physics was pure science. Toward the beginning of that decade I heard the founder of this branch of science, Lord Rutherford, declare in a big meeting that those who believed that nuclear physics would ever be applied were completely out of their mind. And I know that he had in mind particularly one of my friends, Leo Szilard, who had a lot to do with starting work on nuclear energy in the United States. Of course, Lord Rutherford was wrong. Contrary to his expectations nuclear physics became of extreme importance during the war years, and now it is clear to everybody that in war and in peace nuclear energy can and will play a role, which in the course of time is likely to develop into as important a role as electricity itself. This is an instance where the pursuit of pure science, as is often the case, has developed within a short time into something intensely practical.

This fact has helped in establishing the present fashion at all our universities and institutions of higher learning that "puts in the dog-house" anyone who is interested in applications and focuses completely on the pursuit of pure science. The wartime experience helped in this. It was not the only factor that gave rise to the present situation.

There is another way to express this that is not completely polite. You know professors will be professors. And they, like any other group of people, have the firm conviction that they are better than anybody else and that the proper work of a professor in physics is to do the best physics, which is pure physics, which is the most highly fashionable physics. And if a Congressman dares to question us, we professors will tell him unflinchingly that he is stupid. What we are doing and what appears to be impractical today will turn out to be as highly practical as it has turned out to be in the past in the case of atomic energy.

Let us take a step backward and imagine that I have repeated everything that I have stated in the last few paragraphs with the prefix "maybe." *Maybe* pure science will turn into something practical. In fact, I think it will, but the question is: When? Soon, perhaps, and I am one of those who believe that it will—in a couple of centuries. What will happen in the meantime? Let us see what is happening now.

The government is spending a huge amount of money in support of science. I do not know what the exact amount of money is, but $15 billion per annum is a good guess. Ninety percent of this money goes into the support of applied science. At the same time, of the considerable support our government, our foundations, and our states give to universities, more than 90 percent spent for education is in pure science. On the one hand, we are spending a lot of money on applied science; our space effort is one example. On the other hand, we do not prepare our youngsters to participate in this great effort. Our applied science enterprises are starved for really efficient manpower.

This situation is going to get progressively worse. Today many of our applied science endeavors live on past spiritual investment; they utilize those men who have been educated at the time when applied science was not yet despised as it is despised today. When laboratories go out to hire new young people from whom ideas should come, they find practically no reenforcements. The best among the young people, learning from their professors and imitating them, look for academic jobs, for jobs in pure science, even if these offer one half the salary that is available in the field of applied science. One loses prestige, one loses class when one goes into an industrial laboratory or a government laboratory working on applied science. The institutions of applied science get the leavings, and those students whom they get have not been prepared for their jobs. They have to be reeducated.

We still have and we are going to have a few excellent applied science laboratories. As examples, I should like to mention the Bell Telephone Laboratories, where the transistor was developed; I should like to mention to you the laboratories of the IBM company, where the first decisive steps were taken toward the building of our magnificent thinking machines. I should also mention some of the Atomic Energy Commission laboratories. I believe that these excellent laboratories, in spite of heavy odds, will remain excellent. They will be able to persuade at least a few graduates to join them and, if these graduates are insufficiently educated, they will be reeducated.

But, the importance, the impact, of technology on our whole society—on our comforts, on our safety, and our survival—rise year by year. We need more laboratories, and the new laboratories not having the proper staff, not being able to attract excellent people, will never become anything but imitators of what has been done in the past, or what is going on in other places. We are second in space. All the intervening years since Sputnik have not sufficed for us to overcome the head start of the Russians. Isn't $5 billion per year sufficient? I think it is. But the money is not spent in the best way. I do not want to criticize any individual. I am criticizing the fact that not more of our youngsters have gone into this challenging field and that they have not done even better than those who have started the business. Space effort is a growing business. It is a business that can stimulate the imagination, but our imagination does not want to be stimulated.

It is not my job to point out faults except for the purpose of suggesting remedies. The best remedy would be if the trend would change. The best movement is a grass-root movement. But grass-root movements may not arise, and I believe they will not arise spontaneously. The next best possibility is to obtain help from above or from outside. We must realize that something is wrong. We must realize that in the present situation there are grave dangers. Education in applied science should be strongly supported. Let me try to define a little more closely what needs to be done and where our deficiency lies.

Pure science is an activity directed toward the understanding of laws of nature. It is an enormously stimulating, and enormously rewarding, adventure that again and again has resulted in practical applications. It is not due to the wish of concrete improvement of our lot. It is based on one of the most ancient and most valuable impulses—curiosity. You would imagine that in selecting the object of curiosity there should be a wide divergence. On the contrary, it is found that the scientific community makes judgments that define

closely, sometimes all too closely, the main interest in the limited field
in which most fruitful advances can be expected. We are not lacking
in that activity.

On the other end of the spectrum is engineering. To do again what
has been done before, to do it better, to do it more economically and,
last, but by no means least, to do it more safely: this is engineering.
In this field, we are doing reasonably well.

There is a field in between, the field of applied science, where you
do something new, where you have to use your imagination as you
have to use your imagination in pure science. But the aim is something concrete, something useful and durable, and economically justi-
fiable. Whether you will succeed, whether a project in applied science
will lead to a useful end product, you cannot tell. But the work is undertaken with a view to that end product. The examples abound:
aerodynamics, space, nuclear energy, the prediction and influencing
of weather (one of man's oldest endeavors). These are but a few examples. In all of these we see that our competitors are taking a deep
interest, and in many of them they appear to be ahead of us.

One instance that is not in everybody's mind is the field of oceanography. Near each continent there are extended regions, the continental shelves; their area is not very much smaller than the area of
the continents themselves. The geological structure of the continental
shelves is similar to that of the continents. In fact, in past ages these
shelves frequently have been uncovered. The sediments, the mineral
content of these shelves, is not dissimilar to what we find on land. The
economic importance of these shelves is becoming dramatically obvious by the offshore oil exploitations that have begun to spring up in
the Gulf of Mexico. Great discoveries of important gas fields have
just occurred in the sea next to Holland. In the exploration of the
ocean and the ocean bottom the Russians are doing more than any
nation of the world, and this may be one of the main sources of
wealth and of power in the decades to come.

What can we do? What we are beginning to do, rightly, is to pour
more money into our oceanographic institutions. But I claim this is
not enough because these new centers cannot be decently manned,
and, therefore, they will not amount to much. We have to do something about education. If we were in Russia, we could do it by edict;

but we are not and we should not be, and I do not want to get anything done by edict. If this is the tool that we want to employ, we will never catch up with the Russians because, at best, we will use this tool in a clumsy and unexperienced manner. It does not fit into our society. We have to use other means.

I should like to make one modest proposal that perhaps holds a little promise. We do have a number of excellent applied science laboratories. I believe that each of these laboratories must be given an educational job. Every one of these laboratories should undertake the education of students, very particularly the education of graduate students. My experience is that in our system our undergraduate students usually are undecided about their career even at the time they get their Bachelor's degree. They do not yet know what they want to do, what their aim is likely to be. I do not regret that; I do not think that an important question like the planning of one's life-work need be decided at the age of twenty-two. Much less should it be decided, as it is done behind the Iron Curtain, by state authorities. I am deeply convinced that what one wants to do is what one does best.

But what one wants to do depends on the examples before one's eyes. If the example is a professor who has spent his life in the wonderful pursuit of pure science, this is what the young man wants to do. That many of our students turn to pure science I do not regret. That all of our good students should do so is a terrible mistake. I do not want a counter-evolution. I want balance, and I want some of our students to grow up in a surrounding in which the best people—the most successful people—are the ones who have contributed effectively in moving forward the field of applied science. If students grow up in that surrounding they will become applied scientists. And my best definition that I can think of for an applied scientist is that he is the successor of what in the last century we used to call an inventor.

Let me remind you that the best known and the greatest of the American inventors, Edison, pointed the way toward a new style in the inventive process. He realized that invention had become too complex. He could not do it alone, and he built a research institution in which inventions could be worked out by the collaboration of many specialists. That is how inventions like atomic energy, computing machines, and rockets have actually been perfected in recent years.

This fact has a significance with respect to the education an applied scientist must receive. First of all, he must have a general education in the physical sciences. In the embryonic atomic energy project at the beginning of the war, physicists, chemists, mathematicians, and engineers worked together. And the physicist had no idea what the chemists, engineers, or mathematicians were doing, nor could he talk to them, and everyone was ignorant concerning three of the four important disciplines. It is a miracle that we succeeded anyway. But we could have succeeded more easily. Therefore I say that the first prerequisite of an applied scientist is that he should be able to talk the language of any of his future collaborators—of the engineer, of the chemist, of the physicist, of the mathematician.

Beyond that, I advocate that an applied scientist should become excellent in one specialty and write about it a PH.D. dissertation, not only because specialties are needed but also because one specialist can better understand another specialist.

In this way and by introducing properly high standards of education (in collaboration with universities or without collaboration with established universities) our applied laboratories should be given the job to educate the next generation of applied scientists. They should be given the privilege and power to award Masters' degrees and PH.D degrees in applied science. We must create the proper status symbols. There are plenty of youngsters at the age of twenty-one and twenty-two who would flock to these institutions if they were available for the awarding of the highest academic degrees. But as long as our universities do it exclusively, the job is not likely to be done. In some places, like the Massachusetts Institute of Technology, there is a realization of the need. Yet when we tried to distribute fellowships in applied science and I interviewed twenty-four of the most outstanding students, twenty-two of them declared that they really preferred pure science. And MIT is an institute of *technology*.

The right students must be found to receive fellowships, and highly paying fellowships, for applied science. In our applied science laboratories the hunger for good people is so great that a talented bachelor willing to go into applied science can get $10,000 per year, provided he goes into a laboratory and abandons prematurely his academic education. I am not advocating fellowships of $10,000 a year, but I am advocating that those students who were foolish enough or clever enough to marry while they were undergraduates and who have, therefore, some use for money should be given the possibility of living through their graduate fellowship years and become applied scientists in the proper sense. If we do not do all that, if we do not encourage our students financially, and if we do not offer them the right institutions in which they can become applied scientists, then I predict that ten years from now the only valid weather predictions will come from Russia. And twenty years from now, the Russians will determine what the climate will be in the United States. When that happens, the least of the difficulties we shall encounter will be that weather will cease to be a polite topic of conversation.

It seems to me that applied science is not only a part but a vital part of our body politic. This part is in a poor and neglected state. I am not asserting that it is the most important part, but, if we can put our finger on a trouble spot, then we should pay attention to that particular spot. A great American tradition is dying. We must revive it in a form appropriate to the present day.

Beardsley Graham

THE NONPROFIT RESEARCH INSTITUTE:

A NONUNIVERSITY APPROACH

Since 1913, with the endowment of the Mellon Institute in Philadelphia, nonprofit research institutes have been contributing to the advancement and the preeminence of American industry. At the present time there are over fifteen nonprofit research institutes throughout the United States, and the number is growing. In a free enterprise economy that annually sees an amazing rate of failures in almost every business classification, it is most remarkable that not one of these research institutes has even been forced to close its doors. They fulfill a direct and recognized need. They perform a useful, valid function. A substantial and growing market exists among industrial and governmental clients for the services of independent, professionally qualified, and imaginatively managed research groups.

I should add the important note that all of the industrial research institutes are self-supporting. None is permanently underwritten by any group. Each has the obligation to earn an operating surplus, to survive in a competitive business environment, and to grow from its own earnings and the contributions its fund-raising programs bring in.

The nonprofit status of these research institutes means that the respective boards of directors do not represent ownership and do not participate in the earnings of the corporations. This eliminates the potential for conflicts of interest between owners and clients and assures and safeguards independence, plus providing the nonprofits with the freedom and the flexibility to respond quickly to the needs and the opportunities of their clients. The earnings of the nonprofits are reinvested in equipment, staff, and facilities, and a large portion of the earnings is devoted to research projects in the public interest, to scientific meetings, symposiums and publications, and to the support of education.

The present role of the nonprofits has developed through three stages since the establishment of the Mellon Institute and, shortly thereafter, the Battelle Memorial Institute in Columbus, Ohio. The early nonprofits were founded to fulfill the recognized need for applied technological and engineering assistance to industry. The big job during this formative period from 1913 until World War II was to sell research services to industry. Few companies had their own laboratories, and fewer still were willing to undertake the logical development of new products, processes, and techniques. Those companies that did have some in-house capabilities responded to the confidential and competent technical considerations. This combination became known as techno-economics, and its major feature was the utilization of a man with a B.S. in engineering, an M.B.A. in business management, plus actual experience in industry in approaching immediate and practical problems.

The objectives of the nonprofits then became twofold: first, to provide a staff of competent, experienced professionals and creative people who could supply the direct assistance needed by industry and government, and, second, to stimulate and lead industry in charting its own future. Leadership was added to service.

Techno-economics, especially as practiced at Stanford Research Institute, fitted well the patterns of area and regional development and was an extremely useful instrument in helping to create the environment and climate for the attraction of existing companies to a region and for the establishment of new companies and new industries. Techno-economics was also a very profitable operation in that it required an investment in equipment and facilities far below that required for research in the physical sciences.

Although industry's need for applied engineering assistance has diminished, it will remain in the total picture and continue to exert an influence for some time to come. But the type of assistance required is becoming more and more sophisticated. The activities associated with techno-economics are now being supplemented with the skills of the systems scientist and operations research analyst. Systems science, perhaps most easily defined as the application of scientific methods and tools to problems previously handled by experience, judgment, and intuition, is coming into its own right as a form of leadership available to industry and government. The attention of the nonprofits is also being directed more and more toward scientific ideas and less and less toward product development. In any case, we may expect the same sort of change to occur with respect to techno-economics as occurred with respect to applied engineering as more and more companies become proficient in the use of economic analysis and the techniques developed through techno-economics studies.

There are already intimations of the next area of service that the nonprofits will provide their clients—applications in the fields of behavioral and social sciences. Change is today's common denominator, and man is not very successful at accommodating change. Advances in the behavioral and the social sciences will, when translated, interpreted, and applied, allow man to accommodate and accept the vast waves of change that are coming, particularly in the area of man-machine relationships. This predicted activity will bear fruit in direct proportion to the ties that are developed with those doing basic research in these fields.

The third major phase in the development of the nonprofits is now appearing. The nonprofits will still be supplying assistance and leadership, but they will be drawing heavily upon the ideas and knowledge being formulated in basic scientific research of the type that flourishes best in a university environment. They are at the interface of basic and applied research. In the future, the nonprofits will concentrate more and more of their attention on the centers of advanced and postdoctoral research, all the while maintaining within the same organization the capability for both applied economic research and applied engineering research to translate and interpret the scientific information coming from the very frontier of science.

The position of the nonprofits today is quite good. As I mentioned before, none has been forced to close, and I think this speaks most eloquently of their performance over the last fifty years. The total employment at Stanford Research Institute is now at about 2,500, and SRI's dollar volume of annual sales is in the neighborhood of $45 million. Battelle Memorial Institute, with the recent addition of the Atomic Energy Commission's Hanford Laboratories, has an employment figure of nearly 5,000, and contracts for research and development work are coming in at the annual rate of about $70 million. Spindletop Research, of which I am president, has been actively engaged in contract research for just under three years now and is at present doing business at an annual rate of over $2 million. We forecast our growth for the next year at something under 100 percent.

The foundations upon which the nonprofits are built are firm and well-tested. Paradoxical as it may sound, the nonprofits are very profit-oriented; they are accustomed to the timetables and demands or urgent business and industrial environments. Research projects are accomplished thoroughly and efficiently and the results placed before the client in time for him to extract the maximum amount of profit. Also, the nonprofits specialize in knowing what both the right and left hand of basic science are doing. Most companies can be expected to know what is happening in the fields of basic research that have a direct bearing on their own activities. Often, however, advance in fields quite distant can be profitably utilized, and it is the nonprofit research institute that is in the best position to recognize and exploit seemingly unrelated events, to juxtapose unique combinations of knowledge for the benefit of industry.

Setting aside the discussion of the role and the function of the nonprofit research institute for now, let us look at one of the remarkable activities that surrounds the activities of the nonprofits—that of regional economic development. In this connection, I should like to cite the experience of Stanford Research Institute because of my direct contact with it during its formative years. One and one-third million dollars was borrowed to start SRI, $500,000 of it from Stanford University, and the rest from banks and industry. In a very short time, all bank indebtedness was paid off, and the return to Stanford University on its loan is the best investment in its portfolio. SRI grew and spawned more growth around it. Citing a recent report by the Denver Research Institute (another nonprofit, by the way), *International Science and Technology* states that Stanford University and Stanford Research Institute have together been responsible for the spin-off of some twenty new companies, including Varian and Hewlett-Packard.

The spin-off phenomenon has not been confined to the nonprofits.

The University of Michigan has been the origin of fourteen; the University of California's Berkeley campus has been responsible for fifteen; and MIT has been attributed with the creation of between seventy-five and one hundred spin-offs. The interesting point about the spin-offs from university complexes is, according to Denver Research Institute, that the engineering schools rather than the science departments have been the source of the great majority of these new enterprises.

There is a direct cause and effect relationship between advances in scientific research, the ability to apply these advances, and the economic demands of regional development. I am fully convinced that the three are inseparable. Communities, states, and regions that realize that we are emerging into an era of technologically based, science-oriented industry will grow and prosper. Communities, states, and regions that are slow to recognize this trend or try to ignore it altogether will be bypassed in the economic development of the future and, indeed, are being bypassed in the economic development of today.

George B. Kistiakowsky, former Special Assistant to the President for Science and Technology, has said that "the best is vastly more important than the next best . . . and the first rate should always be supported." We are now witnessing the results of that support. Two areas, one on the East Coast stretching from Washington, D.C., to Boston and the other in California, have become the main centers for technologically based industry and are receiving the largest portions of the federal R and D dollar.

This growth and dominance of the East and West Coast regions in this field has been to the detriment of other regions, notably the Midwest, which has experienced a serious net loss of scientific and other creative talent in a cause and effect relationship that has simultaneously found new technically oriented industries locating in other regions. This outflight and overflight can be illustrated by the situation in the states of Illinois and Indiana.

In 1960 Illinois had a population of slightly more than 10 million, or 5.6 percent of the national total, and had 5.2 percent of the nation's scientists. The universities in the state of Illinois graduated about 750 PH.D.s in the 1958–59 school year, or about 74 PH.D.s per million population. This rate is about 50 percent higher than the national average. Over the years nearly one tenth of all the PH.D. scientists in the nation have received their doctorate training in Illinois. No other state except New York has produced more. Right now, only one Illinois-educated PH.D. in five is working in Illinois; the other four have left for more stimulating environments, larger concentrations of industry, and fatter R and D expenditures.

The comparison is even more dramatic in neighboring Indiana. The state of Indiana has 2.6 percent of the nation's population and slightly less than 2 percent of the nation's scientists. Because of Purdue University, Indiana ranks fourth in the nation in the number of PH.D. engineers it produces. And 80 percent of Purdue's PH.D. engineers leave the state. This emigration represents a sizable and unfair drain on the taxpayers of Illinois and Indiana; there is really little practical justification for investing large amounts of tax dollars to train PH.D.s so that they can leave the state and contribute to the economies of other regions. The amount of this contribution is well stated in a rule of thumb developed by Jesse Hobson, Vice President of Southern Methodist University and consultant to a number of nonprofit research institutes: "One PH.D. will generate employment for ten engineers, and those ten engineers will generate employment for 150 technicians, skilled workers, and other support personnel."

I am not suggesting that Illinois and Purdue cut back on their production of PH.D.s by 80 percent. I am suggesting, though, that Illinois, Indiana, and any other state or region that is experiencing a similar outmigration of talent and potential do two things: first, create the ability to apply the work and the research of the best universities to industry; second, through an aggressive public and private program, attract to the area the science-oriented industry that can put this capability to greatest use. The capability for applying basic research need not reside in a nonprofit research institute to be successful. Indeed, there are cases where as little formal activity as the creation of a liberal policy and attitude toward the outside activities and entrepreneurship of the members of a university engineering staff can be enough to make significant differences in the industrial activity and the economy of a region. The formation of an organization such as Purdue's Midwest Applied Science Corporation is a firm and commanding step into the future.

Many studies have indicated that the mild climate and pleasant living conditions in Florida and on the Pacific coast have accounted for the rapid growth of scientific endeavor and personnel in those areas. Along the Atlantic coast, the traditional and growing importance of Boston, New York, and Washington as educational, economic, and political centers has enabled this area to retain and increase its substantial fraction of the nation's creative talent and technically advanced productivity.

Other studies have indicated very strongly that this need not be so. They have listed, in order of relative importance, the considerations in the location of, say, a new research laboratory of a major company.

1. People are more important than places or things.

2. The laboratory should be located where scientists and engineers can enjoy a stimulating intellectual and cultural environment.

3. The laboratory should be no more than a thirty-minute drive to a university where good libraries and a graduate education program are available.

4. Local venture capital should be available. Xerox found their capital in New York after being turned down in Ohio.

Other considerations include the attitudes of the community, the transportation facilities that are available, and the labor force and the support services that are in the area. As you can see, the PH.D. and the research engineer are more interested in their professional well-being than in their physical and material comfort. As things stand now, they can assure their potential for professional development on both the East and West coasts; their physical comfort is the added attraction of the West Coast.

It is possible today to observe a number of influences and effects that significantly modify the situation. For instance, the advent of air conditioning on a mass basis in homes and offices and the substantial problems stemming from overpopulation have definitely contributed to population shifts from California back to the Southwest and the Midwest. Enormous increases in population and industrial activity in

California have resulted in serious water shortages. Air pollution is also creating serious shortages of clean air, and recent statistics reveal that in California alone the clean air that remains is being contaminated with 20 percent of the halogenated hydrocarbons produced in the United States. As part of its price for growth, California now suffers the nation's highest incidence of alcoholics, suicides, and psychiatrists. These are some of the reasons that, as long as ten years ago, persons enjoying economic mobility had begun to leave the West Coast. The trend can be expected to continue, both by individuals and by business establishments. This is the time for the Midwest to start actively recapturing some of the talent it has educated and others have benefited from.

Many states and regions throughout the country are following the same pattern that I have set forth here. In 1958, several individuals got together and founded the Research Triangle Institute. RTI was located on a large tract of land in the center of a triangle drawn between the cities of Raleigh, Durham, and Chapel Hill, North Carolina, and has developed strong ties with the three schools in the area. RTI's research staff is encouraged to accept adjunct professorships at the schools, and the faculties are encouraged to conduct research at RTI. Facilities and information are extensively shared. This recent addition to the nonprofit community now employs some 275 people and conducts business at an annual rate in the neighborhood of $6 million. An announcement was recently made that the National Institutes of Health's Center for Environmental Studies will be located on the RTI campus.

Spindletop Research, once an experiment in boosting the economy of Kentucky, is now a reality. Spindletop was created in December, 1961, by a group of businessmen, industrialists, educators, and state officials who saw the need and the opportunity for an organization that could offer research and development services and leadership to industry and governmental agencies. But Spindletop represents something more than another nonprofit research institute. For the first time, a state government participated in the founding of a nonprofit, realizing an investment in the future by both the public and private sector of the economy. The Kentucky legislature appropriated $3.25 million to Spindletop in the form of land, an administration building, and initial operating capital. Yet, despite the state's participation, Spindletop was established as an independent entity with no formal ties with either the state government or the University of Kentucky, which is also located in Lexington.

The state of Louisiana has recently established the Gulf South Research Institute, patterned exactly after Spindletop. The Louisiana State Legislature has appropriated $7 million for GSRI's start up—$3.5 million for facilities and initial operating funds and another $3.5 million for continuing support over the next seven years. Moreover, GSRI anticipates an additional $3 million appropriation, for a total of $10 million. Private contributions to the success of GSRI have so far amounted to $1 million.

The Mississippi Research and Development Center has been established as an agency of that state, with an appropriation of $1.5 million. The Mississippi Center will be supported by the state legislature at a rate of $1 million per year.

North Star Research Institute in Minneapolis has received over $4.75 million, all from private business and industry. Seventy-four percent of this figure represents stock held by North Star in its own research park of 2,200 acres. The park has seven occupants—a very high figure in these early days when a park with one occupant is considered successful.

I think special mention should be given to the activities of Dallas, Texas, certainly an unlikely place to find a creative, intellectual atmosphere and fast progress toward excellence in graduate programs and the basic research activities of the area's schools. But there it is. The Graduate Research Center of the Southwest was founded in 1961 by a small group of Dallas residents, including the head, Lloyd Berkner, who is often referred to as the father of the International Geophysical Year. GRCSW is now a private, nonprofit corporation and will depend for its support upon private gifts and grants and sponsored research. It is intended to be "an eminent institution for scholarly research and postdoctoral study, to stimulate an atmosphere of graduate excellence" and has purposely been set up so as to prevent isolation. Work at GRCSW will involve the faculties of nearby schools, primarily Southern Methodist University, Texas Christian University, and the University of Dallas. Although postgraduate training leading to a degree will be a part of the program, GRCSW will not grant degrees and must therefore cooperate fully with the schools. Finally, the Graduate Research Center is meant to be a "fountainhead of knowledge" for technically oriented industry in the area.

I think it is appropriate at this time to air some of my views on the universities in general and on the research that is conducted there. I made it plain earlier that the nonprofits, and indeed all of the applied research and development organizations, will have to rely heavily upon the universities and the basic research that is conducted by them. The sad fact is that more basic research is being conducted by industry than by the universities. A lot of research is going on, but of a kind best suited to industry and the applied research organizations. The principal cause of this is the growing dependence of the universities on federal research and development funds.

We can all agree that basic research is a true and proper function of both the educational process and the role of the universities as a provider of new knowledge. But basic research has become confused with just plain research; quantity has become confused with quality.

The universities want the prestige that goes with a large research establishment and the security that goes with a substantial backlog. With this, they can attract top men to their faculties, a better class of graduate students, and, of course, more research. The faculty members themselves, aiming at tenure and accommodating the "publish and prosper" policies of the universities, want to do the type of research that will produce fast and concrete information as long as it is above a certain minimum standard. R and D funds from the federal government satisfy both self-interests. Moreover, federal grants and contracts often have provisions for purchasing the enormously expensive facilities and equipment that characterize research today.

I am afraid, however, that the universities' flirtation with federally sponsored research has all the aspects of a casual love affair; it is an enjoyable, short-term consideration, but it offers no lasting value and the potential for future unpleasantness is inordinately high.

All research must be justified before the expenses will be met. Basic research, where results are impossible to predict and invaluable when they are achieved, can be justified because of its role in the educational process that is necessary to produce the scientific brainpower that will keep this country preeminent. Federal research, on the other hand, must be justified on the basis of investing dollars and getting a return on these dollars. The return may even be in the realm of politics, but there must be a return. Federally sponsored research is therefore mission-oriented, and, although advances in scientific knowledge are sometimes produced as a by-product, the research is designed to lead to specified goals that are known to be reasonably attainable. And the research leading to these goals is more often than not characterized by ingenuity and cleverness. The universities would do well to get back into the business of education and leave ingenuity and cleverness to other organizations.

My desire to see the universities concentrating on basic research and education is based on considerations of the future, and not upon any notions eliminating the competition. The nonprofits have very little competition, and what they do have is manifested primarily in competitive bidding on this or that project. As I made clear earlier, the future of the nonprofits will depend to a great extent on the amount, and particularly the quality, of the basic research that is done in the universities. It remains for others to take the results of this research and disseminate it in the form of contract research projects throughout industry. Our success will depend upon the quality of our staff—educated, you will note, in the graduate programs in basic research at the universities—the universality of our operating philosophies, and techniques of interdisciplinary research.

James S. Triolo

A NEW COMMUNITY OF SCHOLARS

IN THE SOUTHWEST

In May of 1960, a very significant meeting was held in Dallas, Texas, that was attended by a handful of men led by J. Erik Jonsson to discuss a problem and to seek a solution. The problem as they saw it was that the economy in which they were living was in a state of transition from one of basic agriculture to technological industry. The migration to the city that was taking place all over our land was particularly pronounced in the Southwest. The results of the mechanization of agriculture were everywhere apparent; people were leaving the rural areas in droves. One hundred years ago in our country 70 percent of our population received its livelihood from agriculture; today, only 7 percent receive their livelihood from this source; and by 1980 it is predicted that this will drop to 3 percent.

The 1960 census disclosed that 75 percent of the population of Texas is now living in seven or eight urban centers; only 25 percent of the population remains in the rural areas. With this migration of population, the existing industries, including the petroleum industry, were not expanding sufficiently to absorb the transposition of population. Present industry in the Southwest simply was not geared to take care of it.

It became apparent to the Southwestern leaders that there was a critical need for new industry created out of research and technology, an industry of innovation. Obviously as their thinking developed, they learned that such industry requires a strong base of graduate education; this was absolutely essential to make the transition from agriculture to the science-based industry of today. They looked at the

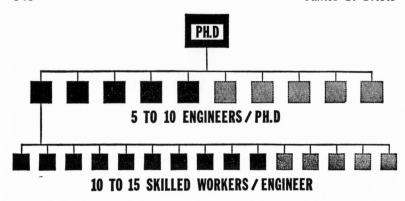

CHART A. *Economic Influence of the Ph.D.*

Massachusetts Institute of Technology and Stanford University and the areas surrounding them and saw what had happened there. They compared these with their own Dallas–Fort Worth area and saw that there was really no strong graduate school in the entire northern section of Texas, no substantial PH.D. producer. And they learned that the PH.D., particularly in the natural sciences and engineering, was the key to the growth of the other areas.

These men learned that the creative and imaginative insights of scientific and technical leaders are at the heart of new products, devices, and methods. They learned further that, in a sense, we are in a race between technological unemployment and new jobs from innovation. Chart A illustrates that the creative, innovating PH.D. and his skills means employment opportunities for many of lesser skills. In fact, the ratio shown is 1 PH.D. to 5-10 engineers, each of whom can create employment opportunities for 10-15 skilled workers. Below this level, of course, we have the semiskilled and the unskilled as the pyramid goes out. The average ratio is about 1 PH.D. to 100 persons of lesser skills, so that we may count at least 100 persons of high skills unemployed in the future for each PH.D. we fail to educate today.

Then the Southwestern leaders looked at the situation across the country to see how the Southwest compared with the rest of the nation in production (if I may use that word) of PH.D.s. In 1962 the origin of these degrees in all fields shows great concentration in the East, the Midwest, and the Far West; the Southeast and the Southwest are lagging far behind the rest of the nation in graduate education. (See Chart B.) Texas, for example, shows 36 PH.D.s conferred in 1962 per million population compared with a national average of 65 per million population. We believe the optimum is around 100. So Texas alone will have to double its present production of doctoral degrees to equal the average and treble it to achieve the optimum. The main points are that all but one of the leading graduate universities are in the East, the Midwest, and the Far West and that these institutions produce two thirds of the total PH.D.s. So we may conclude that academic achievement, using the PH.D. as a yardstick, is obviously concentrated in these three areas.

Now let us look at the implications of this concentration of doctoral power shown in Chart C. In 1962–63 the twenty big doctoral universities produced 53 percent of all PH.D.s in the country. And twenty universities are the largest recipients of federal research support, with $532 million, or 60 percent of the total (not including off-campus facilities such as Argonne, Lawrence Radiation, or Lincoln

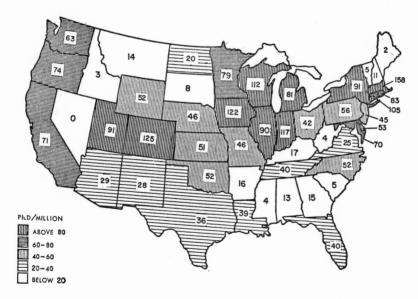

CHART B. *Doctorates Conferred, 1962 (per million population)*

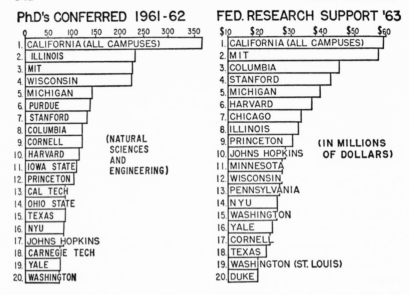

CHART C. *Comparison of Ph.D. Degrees Conferred in 1961–62
with Federal Research Support in 1963*

laboratories). It is interesting to note that fifteen of the largest producers of PH.D.s are also among the twenty universities that attract
the largest amout of research dollars. And only one of them, the
University of Texas, is in the Southwest. With the explosion of population in the Southwest within the next ten years, we should be able to
generate at least four or five graduate universities that would rank in
the top twenty.

The conclusion that our Southwestern leaders reached is that research dollars go where concentrations of brainpower are trained in
research and that there are precious few in the Southwest. With these
problems in mind, they turned to possible solutions. The solution they
selected was to establish a private, nonprofit center for basic research
in the natural sciences and postdoctoral training, the Graduate Research Center of the Southwest. They realized fairly early that this
should include not only Texas but the surrounding states. When they
brought Lloyd Berkner to the presidency of the Center, he broadened

the scope and the concept to a regional one covering the entire Southwest.

I should like to present in some detail the Center's concept, its mission, program, benefits to education and industry, financing, and its new campus—in other words, the why, the what, the how, the when, the where, and the how much.

The two basic objectives, I repeat, are new knowledge from basic research and the advancement of graduate education in the entire region through cooperative programs with the existing colleges and universities of the area. I shall explain these arrangements in more detail later. I should like to stress two points, however. First, we are working in cooperation with these universities and with industry and not in competition with them; our role is one of catalyst to generate doctoral capacity within the existing institutions. Second, although we are permitted to do so by our charter, as a matter of policy we do not confer degrees because it could then be contended that we are in competition with the institutions with which we are trying to collaborate.

According to the organizational plan of the Center, we shall establish five interdisciplinary laboratories, without rigid departmental walls, to encourage a free interchange among laboratories and divisions. (See Chart D.) The research scientist is the faculty member, with faculty rank and status. Academic policy is developed by an academic committee on which faculty with tenure are represented. Proposed appointees are thoroughly reviewed by this academic committee. Fifty percent of our board members are heads of academic institutions in the region.

At present we are organizing our Laboratory of Material Sciences and making progress with our Laboratory of Molecular Sciences. We started with a Laboratory of Earth and Planetary Sciences in 1962. The first man on board was Frank Johnson, former scientist at Lockheed Aircraft Corporation in California. In October, 1963, Carl Kossack, formerly of IBM, started our Laboratory of Computer Sciences, and we have now as head of our Genetics Division, Carsten Bresch, an eminent geneticist from Cologne, Germany. His team has moved from Germany to join us in Dallas in setting up this division.

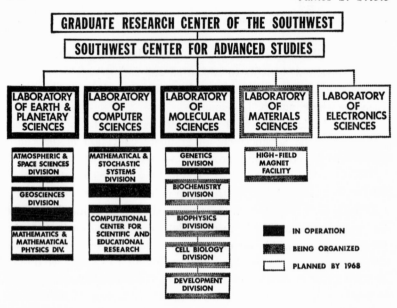

CHART D. *Organization Chart of the Graduate Research Center of the Southwest*

Let us consider the interaction with universities of the area. This, of course, is the second basic mission of the Center. The early steps are depicted in Chart E. Some of them represent strong programs, some merely the first tentative steps. In the program at Southern Methodist University in geophysics seven of our geoscientists spent a year with the SMU faculty planning the program and implementing it and are now teaching in it. Ten doctoral candidates are presently enrolled and SMU calculates that it is probably six to eight years ahead of its time schedule in having a doctoral program in this field as a result of the collaboration from our people. Again, I repeat that this is a regional approach to solving many problems of graduate education and that the Center serves as a catalyst in the total effort to advance graduate education. The advantages of the interdisciplinary laboratory are illustrated by the interrelationship between our Laboratory of Earth and Planetary Sciences and the departments of physics, mathematics, space sciences, oceanography, and relativity theory in five institutions. This type of organization, without strict departmental divisions, gives us great flexibility in working with the traditional departments of the existing universities.

I should like to describe briefly our educational programs.

Postdoctoral training is our primary educational effort; at the present time we have twenty-four postdoctorals with us from several schools around the nation and from abroad. They have two-year appointments as research associates.

Joint doctoral programs are the type such as I described in geophysics with SMU, and we hope to extend this into other areas.

Summer programs are designed for undergraduates and faculty of the region so that they can be exposed not only to our faculty but to visiting professors from outside the region.

Teaching in the universities is another feature. When our faculty members receive their appointments, they understand that they are to do some teaching and that this can vary from one half to one third of their time. It is a part of their basic assignment in coming to the Cen-

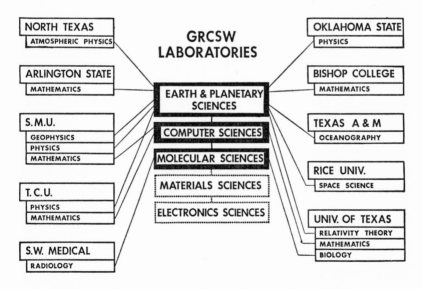

CHART E. *Interactions of the Graduate Research Center of the Southwest with Southwestern Universities*

ter. This can be at either the graduate or the undergraduate level and for the present has been pretty well restricted to the area immediately around Dallas–Fort Worth.

Special regional projects are planned. We have one project going in oceanography, based at Texas A. and M. University. We are planning a data link with several of the schools in the area to provide cooperative library service in the north Texas area.

Research by doctoral candidates is another program. By special agreement, doctoral candidates from the schools in the area may come to the Center to do their dissertation research under the leadership of our faculty people. Our supervising faculty member is then appointed to the committee of the doctoral candidate at his home university and participates in his examination. But the degree is conferred by the home university and not by us.

Seminars, conferences, and symposia are also part of our program. These range from local seminars, to which we always invite not only the academic personnel of the area but the scientists from industry as well, to conferences of a state-wide and regional nature, and we have held two very successful international symposia.

The Center provides benefits to industry: the trained minds and new knowledge of which institutions of higher learning are the only source. Another benefit actually flows in both directions: consulting services provided by our faculties in the applied research and development problems of science-based industry, and industry sending its scientists back to the Center with fundamental questions or for advanced training in their disciplines.

At the end of 1964 we had 246 persons on the staff and faculty, and at present we have about 275. We plan that this will reach 350 by the end of 1965. This depends, of course, on our obtaining the necessary resources. We are trying to hold the percentage of administration and service personnel down to a maximum of 30 percent so that when we reach about 1,000 total personnel in 1968, there will not be more than 300 of such personnel.

Another major point I should like to stress is that we will bring scientists and faculty members from outside the Southwest. We will not take anyone from the faculty of a Southwestern university because, in our mind, this would merely be a reshuffling of the brainpower of the Southwest rather than a net addition to it. We think of the latter as our basic objective.

We believe that the swarming principle has begun. Of our 72 faculty appointments, 70 have their PH.D.s, and we are starting to attract very distinguished people to what was once called an "intellectual desert."

The Center is located in North Central Texas in the Denton–Fort Worth–Dallas triangle, which demographers predict will grow into one metropolitan area of three to five million persons by 1975. Obviously this area will need at least two or three great graduate centers where it now has none.

The Center's campus is in the community of Richardson, just north of Dallas, and central to this activity. In Denton there are two institutions, Texas Woman's University and North Texas State University; in Fort Worth, Texas Christian University; in Arlington, Arlington State College, which has just become a branch of the University of Texas; and in Dallas, Southern Methodist University, the University of Dallas, and Bishop College, a Negro college that has recently moved to Dallas. These are our immediate neighbors and are the institutions we are serving first, although we hope to expand our activities through the state and the region. We feel that we are central not only to this area but to the entire region. In brief, we are strategically located.

Our 1,266-acre campus is located about twenty minutes from downtown Dallas on the expressway. About 25 percent of the land is reserved for educational purposes. The remaining land will be used for related facilities. We shall invite the industrial laboratories of industry into this area and hope to build something like Boston's Route 128 or the Stanford Industrial Park at Palo Alto. We may set up our own applied research laboratory in addition to the basic research of the Center. Immediately to the north we have a neighbor—the Dallas North Industrial Park. This is a venture by a Texas industrialist who has seen what has happened at Route 128 and Stanford and wants to be close to the source of fundamental research. He is developing a research park of 1,300 additional acres. He has three research laboratories of industrial firms on his land at present. We have three more ready to come to our land as soon as our planning is completed.

We have completed and are occupying our first laboratory building. This is called the Founder's Building, and we hope to build three additional research laboratories like it. The central core facility, around which the laboratories will be built, will house an auditorium, library, conference and seminar rooms, administrative offices, food service, and so forth. The first laboratory building cost about $3 million and has 116,000 square feet of floor space. It has the very remarkable flexibility of modular construction, which is readily changeable or expandable for multi-use purpose. The buildings are tightly grouped to permit easy interchange, good access, and communications. This, then, is our research campus.

It has been estimated that over the period 1963–68, the Center will cost $65 million for capital expenditures and operations. It has been contended that this is an underestimate, that our plan is so ambitious that it will cost $200 million. But at least on the present projection, we plan to spend approximately $40 million for sponsored research, of which we estimate 80 percent will come from government sources and 20 percent from industrial sources. We shall spend $20 million on land, buildings, and equipment and $5 million on educational and general expenses, start-up costs and unsponsored research. The sources of this $65 million will be as follows: $40 million from government and industrial sources for the sponsored research; $5 million pledged by the citizens and industry of Dallas in 1963 to get us started; and $20 million through a national development program from private sources—individuals, foundations, and corporations. Dallas now has got us off the ground, and we have to move to statewide, regional, and national sources for this additional help. These sources of income do not include three items: the initial guarantees of the three founders—an undisclosed amount of money running to several million dollars; income from land leases or sales—much like the way the Stanford University has developed its industrial park; and income from our educational program in the form of fees for teaching by our faculty in the regional universities.

Frederick Seitz

THE UNIVERSITY: INDEPENDENT

INSTITUTION OR FEDERAL SATELLITE?

Twenty-five years ago the American university, after a long period of relative detachment from governmental affairs, formed deep ties to the government, mainly through its activities in science and engineering, under the pressures of World War II. It should be mentioned, of course, that, prior to this, the federal government had at various times displayed deep interest in the institutions of higher learning. For example, the Morrill Act, passed in 1862, provided federal land in support of a number of colleges and universities. This step was followed by federal grants in support of agricultural research in universities. Still later, most universities established military training units on either a required or optional basis.

The transition in relationships with the government that began about 1939 or 1940 signified, however, the development of far deeper ties between the typical faculty member in science and engineering and his federal government. In effect, he came to regard the federal government as something in the nature of a specialized customer for the output of his own work, rather than as a general sponsor of his activities like those who contribute to the general endowment of the university.

I was a young faculty member at the University of Pennsylvania at that period and recall very vividly the transition which began with the creation of advisory research links to the Army and Navy and ultimately flowered into contract support for research through the National Defense Research Committee (NDRC) and the Office of Scientific Research and Development (OSRD). Almost overnight those scientists and engineers whose work had obvious meaning to the course of military technology found themselves passing from the condition of material poverty of the depression to a state in which funds for equipment and travel were as ample as reason could expect. Many of us who were caught up in all of this prosperity fully expected the situation to revert to the prewar state of affairs once the war ended. Instead, the flow of money to the universities has continued to grow and broaden ever since 1945, doubling on the average every four years, so that the amount of money supporting pure and applied research in universities is now about thirty times larger than it was at the end of the war. One may reasonably ask to what extent the academic scholars involved may have sold their souls to achieve this flood of gold. Have they, for example, sacrificed precious freedom of choice for material well-being?

In attempting to analyze the effects of federal support upon the universities, one may recognize three distinct periods of time, namely, (1) the wartime period between 1939 and 1945, (2) the period, between 1945 and 1960, of evolution of individual contract grants for research, and, finally, (3) the period since 1960, characterized by the emergence of what is sometimes called "big science."

The wartime period, being one of great national emergency, followed what might be termed a natural course in which the practicalities of the war overwhelmed everything else. The universities in one way or another became transformed into arsenals to the extent that they could be useful in the war effort. The most remarkable aspect of the situation, viewed in retrospect, is that the national policies that were developed for using the academic scientists and engineers were so highly rational. This pattern, while, of course, by no means accidental, grew, oddly enough, out of a study made during the depth of the depression by a group of leading scientists and engineers of ways in which the scientific community might be put to work in the national interest to help pull the country out of the depression. This study, which was conducted under the auspices of the National Academy of Sciences as the result of a request from the White House, was directed by Karl T. Compton, then president of the Massachusetts Institute of Technology. The recommendations were not put into effect when they were made available in 1935. They were, however, picked up again under a modified guise in 1939 and 1940 when President Roosevelt turned to essentially the same group of leaders for help in connection with the war effort. Thus, a two-year study made during the doldrums of the depression led to the creation of the NDRC and the OSRD in the early years of the war and made it possible for academic scientists and engineers, as well as others, to render their professional services to their government in time of war with the absolute minimum of impedance from civilian or military bureaucrats.

During the war relatively little thought was given by the universities to the influence of federal support on institutional policies, because most university staffs not only were absorbed in war activities but also felt that the flow of government contract money would stop promptly at the end of the war. Most of us hoped only that we would be permitted to keep some reasonable fraction of the equipment and related facilities that had been accumulated during the war.

It is also worth noting that there was relatively little complaint at that time from those outside the fields of physical science and engineering regarding the preferred treatment accorded those fields during the war because it was generally recognized that they had immediate practical importance. Still further, many biologists turned their attention to the physical sciences rather than to their own fields because the former often seemed somewhat more germane to the issues of the war.

The fact that the current of money kept flowing to the universities after the war, and indeed grew in volume, rested on two circumstances. First, the executive and legislative branches of the government felt that the scientific community deserved some form of continuing support as reward for its effective work during the war and agreed to establish a National Science Foundation, in accordance with the recommendations of a committee under the chairmanship of Vannevar Bush, contained in its report, "Science—the Endless Frontier." Second, federal agencies with applied missions, such as the Department of Defense, the Atomic Energy Commission, and the National Institutes of Health, decided their missions would be furthered substantially by retaining a close tie to the academic community. As a result, project support was continued in universities after

the war on a scale that had no precedent before 1939. Fortunately for
the academic community, the group of scientific administrators who
held key posts in the governmental agencies at the end of the war
were highly enlightened and promptly set up procedures for administering project support in the universities that would give the individual scientist a high degree of freedom and flexibility in his work. The
group of civilians and officers who established the Office of Naval
Research in 1946 constituted a particularly farsighted and inspired
group. In many ways they set the pattern for the evolution of project
support that occurred between 1945 and 1960.

Let me describe in some detail the principal features of the pattern
of support that prevailed in the decade and a half following 1945.
The following are probably the most important characteristics.

1. Almost all good scientists in universities were able to obtain
with reasonable speed either contracts or grants with one or more
agencies for research close to their own interests. The funds provided
could be used for equipment, stipends for advanced research students
or technicians, visiting research scientists, and travel. Initially, the
physical scientists and engineers were given precedence over the biologists, but this inequity disappeared with the growth of the grant program of the National Institutes of Health and the development of the
National Science Foundation.

2. Although the funds involved in the contracts and grants passed
through the administrative offices of the university, they were usually
directed very specifically to the working scientist who generated the
proposals for his support and maintained close liaison with the governmental agencies. While this pattern of dispersal of funds within the
university, which was quite different from that which had prevailed
before 1939, had little effect on the relations between faculty and administration in many of the well-established universities, it did alter
such relationships very profoundly in some institutions. Before the
war, the administration of the university had the prime responsibility
for generating the funds needed for the work of the faculty. In the
new pattern of project support, which focused attention on the individual faculty member, it became possible for the recipient of funds
derived from contracts or grants to look upon the administration as a
channel providing necessary but relatively routine service. In fact, in

some institutions the administration was willing to tailor its policies to conform with the interests of the more affluent and influential research investigators in order to keep the money flowing. Fortunately, most institutions have managed to keep this trend under reasonable control. I wish to emphasize that in my own experience the federal agencies have played an essentially passive role in bringing about the changes in relationship between faculty and administration in those cases in which they have occurred. Generally speaking, the university has little difficulty in compelling the federal agencies to subscribe to those sound and reasonable principles that it chooses if the university holds its ground and works in concert with others. Those universities that have permitted the flow of funds from contracts and grants to have a substantial effect on their internal policies have done so by inanition, if not volition.

3. Although the typical competent university scientist or engineer has had relatively free access to research money in the period between 1945 and 1960, the same cannot be said of the scholars in the social sciences and humanities, particularly the latter. This does not mean that those outside of science and engineering have not profited substantially from the affluence of the academic community since the war. It does mean, however, that their well-being has tended to lag behind that in the fields somewhat closer to the technical arts. Fortunately, the impending shortage of university faculty in all branches seems to guarantee that the universities will find it necessary to generate the means to support all forms of good scholarship on a more or less equitable, competitive basis. It is even possible that the federal government will eventually establish a National Humanities Foundation to accelerate the establishment of a more balanced situation.

4. Since Congress has, in general, treated the mission-oriented agencies somewhat more generously over the years than it has the National Science Foundation, certain fields of science have advanced at the expense of others at various times. For example, neither the Department of Defense nor the Atomic Energy Commission was inclined to support cosmic ray physics during the first decade or so after the war, although they were prepared to support nuclear and accelerator physics generously. As might be expected, cosmic ray research was somewhat stifled until this imbalance was rectified. Sim-

ilarly, the strong support given to biochemistry by the National Institutes of Health has caused that field to grow to some degree at the expense of physical, inorganic, and organic chemistry in the last decade and a half. It should be emphasized, however, that effects of this type are distinctly second order in nature. Few brilliant and dedicated scientists have been prevented from following a path of their own choosing for any extended period of time, even though some degree of patience may be required now and then.

5. The geometric growth with time of governmental funds available for universities, when coupled with the fact that a fraction of such funds are used for faculty salaries by some universities, has transformed the academic hiring hall into an employees market. A good scientist has been able to go more or less where he pleases and, in general, to carry his project support with him. Generally speaking, he has been in a strong bargaining position since the war and has expected the university to mold its policies to his wishes. Among other things this has permitted him to gratify whatever concepts of status and independence he may value. In a statistical sense this trend has, among other things, had the effect in many universities of removing many of the most distinguished faculty members farther away from the undergraduate student. While there are notable exceptions to this rule, a far larger fraction of the most distinguished scientists in the universities now satisfy their formal teaching requirements by giving a graduate seminar course than was the case before 1939. Many undergraduate students in our larger universities are well along in their four-year undergraduate program before they have anything resembling intimate association with the ablest faculty members on their campuses.

6. It is very important to emphasize that the money that has been channeled into the university system since the war through the government pattern of contracts and grants has incidentally given the universities much of the vitality that they have needed in order to prepare to handle the enormous demand for higher education that is now emerging so clearly in our society. Without some substantial form of federal support in the postwar decades, it is quite likely that the universities would have faltered and been in a far less able position to face the inundation of qualified students that they expect in the coming decade. One might have achieved the same level of competence

and capability by giving the money to the universities in other ways; in fact, it is quite possible that the universities would be even better prepared to handle the tasks ahead had they received the support in ways other than through the project system. However, it would be very difficult to take the viewpoint that the universities would be as well able to serve the national welfare in the period ahead had they not received the increased support made possible by federal funds.

I hope I have made it clear that I believe that the vast amount of federal money that went to the universities between 1945 and 1960 has, on the whole, been enormously beneficial, with the advantages truly overwhelming the disadvantages by far. This is not to say that the project system has been a perfect one; in fact, I think we are now moving into an era in which the imperfections could well be disastrous in certain areas, as I shall describe more definitely later. In my opinion, the greatest defects of the project system center, first, in the inequities of the selective support given to the sciences and the humanities—inequities that rest on quite basic attitudes prevalent in our society rather than upon skillful political intrigue by the scientist; second, on the circumstance that the project system has tended to denigrate the highly important role of the university administration in establishing policy; and, third, on the fact that the system has made it possible for some of the faculty members in the university community to become very far removed from the life of the undergraduate student.

The first of these weaknesses can be corrected only by the creation of special funds derived from federal, state, or private sources to support the humanities. As you know, there are several bills now before Congress to create a National Humanities Foundation. It is much too early to predict how they will fare. I am inclined to the opinion that the project system is not well suited to the support of the social sciences and humanities. It would be far better if federal funds intended for such fields were given to the universities in the form of block institutional grants to be dispersed by each university in accordance with policies that the institution evolves. Needless to say, one would expect some broad regulatory policies to emanate from the federal government as well. These policies should be of a general nature, designed to guarantee that the money is used for the purposes intended

—perhaps to circumscribe the fraction that can be used to support the salaries of the tenure faculty. Unless the funds are provided in the form of block institutional grants, I believe that the federal agency responsible for disbursing them will find itself hopelessly enmeshed in the process of attempting to justify individual studies before Congressmen who may often feel that they should seek out something in the nature of an obvious applied mission for each study. As you know, one has already encountered a certain amount of difficulty in supporting science through the project system on this score, even though the strength of our society is now very largely based on the practical fruits of fundamental science.

To emphasize this point further, I think that the whole process of supporting academic research with federal funds would be improved substantially if a larger fraction of the money granted by the government came to the universities in the form of institutional grants that were handled on the basis of decisions made jointly by university administration and faculty. It seems to me that such a system would put the relationship between administration and faculty back into proper perspective and make it more apparent that the two sides of the university structure have a common goal in the evolution of the university and its work. Among other things, it would elevate the positions of dean and department head to a status such that those occupying these posts would once again be involved in a critical way in decision-making on the distribution of university funds, much as was the case before 1939. At the present time most of the deans and department heads, instead of being granted authority commensurate with their responsibilities, must find their reward tied in a highly diffuse manner to their deep sense of loyalty to the institution that they serve. The project system, which tends to direct money to the individual faculty member over the heads of the administrative officers, has a tendency to reduce the status of deans and department heads to that of clerks.

Many of my faculty friends object strenuously to the view I have just expressed. They fear that their activities would become subject to arbitrary decisions by the university administration if its role in deciding the allocation of funds were enlarged. To them I can only say that the success of the project system between 1945 and 1960 depended to no small extent on the presence in the federal agencies of a very remarkable group of scientific administrators. I have no confidence that this quality can be maintained indefinitely in the future as the pattern of incentives and ideals changes from one generation to the next. It is high time that faculty and administration learn to handle institutional grants in a way that serves the goals of both in the light of the welfare of the university as a whole. There are many examples of institutions in which such a pattern of decision has worked. I see no basic reason for pessimism as long as sufficient time is available to develop a new system.

In the foregoing discussion you will note that I have tended to treat the decade and a half between 1945 and 1960, the second of the three periods mentioned in the introduction, as distinct from the previous five years. It seems to me that the more recent period (1960 to date) belongs to a new era for a number of reasons that up to now may have been more clearly evident to the physical scientist than to the life scientist.

One characteristic of the new era is that "big science" has emerged on the scene in a predominant way and has tended to occupy more and more of the attention of the scientific administrators in the agencies, partly because the sums of money needed for big science are relatively great and partly because of the special glamour associated with such projects. By big science I mean, of course, programs that require very large and very costly items of equipment, such as high energy accelerators, large astronomical observatories, oceanographic vessels, large nuclear reactors, and large rocket boosters. It is quite clear that such items of equipment, and the associated large teams of scientific investigators and technicians, are indispensable for the advance of science on certain frontiers. The dangers associated with them lie in the fact that they tend to divert attention and money away from the independent investigator, whose work is also indispensable to the advance of science. Moreover, when large installations are attached to a single university, they tend to unbalance the institution, since they lead to the development of a large administrative structure that may find itself working at cross purposes to the goals of those dedicated to the university's principal mission, namely, education— education here being used in a very broad sense.

Closely coupled with the rising trend of emphasizing big science has been the drift of the attention of some agencies toward relatively strongly mission-oriented programs and away from basic science. For example, the Department of Defense, which gave the initial thrust to the project support of the basic physical sciences in the first decade after the war, now focuses its attention in the basic sciences mainly on mission-oriented programs such as oceanography. The Atomic Energy Commission (AEC), it is true, has become the principal supporter of high energy physics in the country. On the other hand, the Joint Congressional Committee on Atomic Energy has recently suggested to Donald Hornig, the President's Special Assistant for Science and Technology, that it might be desirable to put this program in a separate funding category so that it could be reviewed independently of the more mission-oriented work of the AEC, which the Joint Committee feels should not be placed in direct competition with the requests for more basic science.

In brief, I believe that there is a clear indication, at least in the physical sciences, that the agencies of the federal government, including the science administrators, are diverting more and more of their attention from programs involving project support of individual scientists to items of big science. Necessary though this trend may be if certain important aspects of science are to advance, I am inclined to feel that the typical faculty scientist who works on a relatively small scale will face disaster unless the techniques to provide him with support become more securely built into the system of federal funding. Again, it seems to me that the solution to this problem lies in the growth of the institutional grants that are disbursed within the campus on the basis of decisions made within the university, rather than on the basis of decisions made on a case-by-case basis by the science administrators in the federal agencies.

In discussing these problems with the life scientists, I have found that at the present time they regard them as something in the nature of abstractions because the project system is still working well in their fields. Neither have programs in big science emerged so prominently to the fore as yet, nor have the agencies responsible for the life sciences, particularly the National Institutes of Health, faced the budget ceilings encountered by some of the other agencies. It would be very surprising, however, if the life sciences do not encounter the same problems as the physical sciences within the next decade.

One of the phenomena associated with the evolution of big science has been the stirring among universities of a search for techniques for administering large facilities in a way that will allow faculty members from a number of institutions to share in the use of such facilities on an equitable basis. The oldest prominent organization of this type is, of course, the Associated Universities, Inc., created in 1946 by nine eastern universities to develop and administer what is now the Brookhaven National Laboratory. It seems safe to say that this technique will be explored in depth throughout the country during the present decade and that it will be expanded as it becomes more and more clear that single-university management of large facilities provides an increasingly unsatisfactory way of handling large laboratories that are to be used for basic research by participants from a number of universities.

One is sometimes asked if the difficulties that have occurred on the campus of the University of California at Berkeley and that are reflected in one way or another in many parts of the country can be ascribed in substantial part to the fact that institutions have received so much federal money. The campus syndrome is, of course, a very complicated one and cannot be explained simply in a sentence or two.

Personally, I believe that the difficulties on our campuses that have been dramatized most vividly by the events at Berkeley originate from a sequence of factors, among which the flow of federal money to universities is a minor one in the sense that the turbulence would be precisely the same if federal money were replaced by funds from state or private sources. At the present time the attitudes of the students, the faculty, the administration, and the trustees toward their university are vastly more important in the creation of the present tensions than is the attitude of those in Washington who determine the flow of money to universities. In brief, the Berkeley syndrome is the product of affluence, a complex and not necessarily orderly stirring on the campus as a result of diverse interpretations of the vision of the Great Society and profound changes in the motivations of American youth, all mingled with the traditional rebellion of youth toward the established order. It is possible that the ease with which faculty members can procure funds from the government on a personal project basis has added fuel to the conflagration by giving faculty members a larger sense of independence from the opinions of administration and the trustees. On the other hand, in our history, whenever the universities have been near the center of the national stage, the university faculties seem always to have shown some spirit of rebellion. Taking the situation as a whole, it would appear that federal money has played a role in it only to the extent of making those connected with the university feel that what takes place on our campuses is important to the nation, thus permitting them to take their causes very seriously.

To summarize, it is my personal opinion that the decision of the federal government to give support to our universities on a large scale after the war has been enormously beneficial both to the universities and to our country at large. It has kept the universities viable and has placed them in a far better position to handle the difficult problems that they will face in the future of dispensing higher education of quality on a mass level. There have obviously been substantial flaws in the system. None of these, however, have been fatal. All can be remedied with the proper application of intelligence and patience. The project system that had worked so effectively in the war was used successfully for about a decade and a half after the war but is now beginning to lose its effectiveness as the agencies and Congress become diverted by the glamour of big science. It is my personal opinion that the only effective remedy is to put more and more of the money for independent investigators into institutional grants to be dispersed internally by the universities themselves.

It is clear that the time has come when the federal government can enhance the health of the universities further by providing support for the social sciences and humanities. For several good reasons, it seems to me that it would be wise to initiate such support on an institutional rather than a project basis from the start and thereby avoid some of the problems that the natural sciences now face.

I realize that some people will think that I have adopted far too pragmatic a view of government-university relations in this paper and have not focused sufficiently on some of the more intangible aspects of university life, such as those related to academic freedom and free speech. The simple truth of the matter is that in my own experience I have not found any desire on the part of officers of the federal agencies to interfere with the university in connection with these more intangible aspects of academic life. It seems to me that the universities have as much leeway to establish and maintain their traditions as they did before the war. Any flaws that exist as a result of the flow of federal money lie, for the most part, at the doorstep of the institutions and of those who tenant them.

Alvin M. Weinberg

BUT IS THE TEACHER ALSO A CITIZEN?

My subject is the connection between the university, particularly the scientific university, and society. In so far as this connection affects the university's interests and its manner and style of teaching, I am concerned with the question "But is the teacher also a citizen?" The tensions and contradictions I see in the relation between the modern scientific university and society are much the same as those described by others, but I describe them in a slightly different language, a language that comes from my own nonuniversity world.

Perhaps I should explain what this language is. I come from a large government laboratory. The laboratory is organized into sixteen scientific divisions, each of which is concerned with a particular scientific discipline—that is, each is "discipline-oriented." But the primary purpose of the laboratory is to accomplish applied missions—desalting the sea economically, or providing an inexhaustible, cheap, energy source, or alleviating radiation disease. The laboratory as a whole is "mission-oriented." Thus our laboratory, like so many other institutions, has a dual structure—organizationally it is discipline-oriented; functionally it is mission-oriented. To accomplish each mission we establish projects that cross divisional, disciplinary lines. A large project can involve a dozen divisions. This mission-discipline duality is evident in many social structures, not only large laboratories. I see the relations between the university and society in terms of this duality.

THE MISSION-DISCIPLINE DUALITY

Our society is mission-oriented. Its mission is resolution of problems arising from social, technical, and psychological conflicts

This paper appeared in *Science* 149 (August 6, 1965), 601–6.

and pressures. Since these problems are not generated within any single intellectual discipline, their resolution is not to be found within a single discipline. Society's standards of achievement are set pragmatically: what works is excellent regardless of whether or not it falls into a neatly classified discipline. In society the nonspecialist and synthesizer is king.

The university by contrast is discipline-oriented. Its viewpoint is the sum of the viewpoints of the separate, traditional disciplines that constitute it. The problems it deals with are, by and large, the problems generated and solved within the disciplines themselves. Its standards of excellence are set by and within the disciplines. What deepens our understanding of a discipline is excellent. In the university the specialist and analyst is king.

The structure of the discipline-oriented university and the structure of the mission-oriented society tend to be incongruent. Moreover, as the disciplines making up the university become more complex and elaborate in response to their own internal logic, the discrepancy between university and society grows. The university becomes more remote; its connection with society weakens; ultimately it could become irrelevant. The growth of this discrepancy appears to me to be a central problem in the relation between the university and society. It poses major difficulties for the university professor, especially in the natural sciences, who views broadly his responsibility as a citizen.

Harvey Brooks, Dean of Engineering and Applied Physics at Harvard University, put the matter with his usual incisiveness:

The . . . issue is the relationship between science and technology in education. The original concept of an engineering school, as of a medical school, was an association of practitioners who used the benefit of their varied experience to teach young people. This tradition is somewhat maintained to this day in the field of architecture, but in both medicine and engineering the importance of the underlying sciences has become so great that medical and engineering faculties are increasingly populated with basic scientists who do research or teaching in sciences which are relevant to but by no means identical with the practice of medicine or engineering. The old form of teaching primarily by practicing physicians or engineers was found wanting because practical knowledge was too rapidly being made obsolete by new scientific developments which could not be fully absorbed or appreciated by the mature practitioner. Yet in the process something of the spirit and attitude of the skilled practitioner was lost, particularly *his willingness to deal with problems whole rather than in terms of the individual contributing disciplines.* . . . In medicine this problem has been partially met by the teaching hospital, but in engineering the analog of the teaching hospital is the big engineering development laboratory in industry. How, then, is the spirit of applied science and engineering to be retained in engineering education? The intellectual foundations of engineering lie increasingly in the basic sciences; inevitably engineering faculties will contain large numbers of people whose way of thinking is more akin to that of the scientist than the engineer. It is these people that will develop many of the techniques which will be used by the engineer of the future. And it is their knowledge, not that of the current engineer, which the student will be using ten years from now. The reconciliation of these two necessary attitudes of mind in the process of engineering education is the central dilemma of the field today.[1]

THE TREND TOWARD PURITY

Though Dean Brooks's critique is directed mainly at the engineering school, what he says has a wider relevance. The university's disciplinary viewpoint and even organization create many points of tension between the university and the society in which it is embedded.

One is the tendency toward increasing "purity," especially in the sciences and most notably in mathematics. I would measure purity of a branch of science by the degree to which the phenomena studied are of intrinsic interest to that science or are of extrinsic interest. In the first instance, the science is more pure; in the second, where the motivation is to understand phenomena that lie outside that branch of science, the science is less pure. Thus I would divide science into pure, or intrinsically motivated, and applied, or, more broadly, extrinsically motivated. For example, applied science (in the usual sense of the term) seeks to clarify some aspect of, say, engineering or medicine: we study the chemistry of molten fluorides at Oak Ridge because we wish to build a reactor that uses molten fluorides; or we study certain viruses because these viruses are implicated in certain kinds of leukemia.

---

[1] "The Dean's Report, 1963–1964," *Harvard Engineers and Scientists Bulletin,* No. 45 (1964), p. 6. The italics are mine.

Extrinsically motivated science also includes those sciences that are pursued in order to deepen our understanding of some other branch of even pure science. For example, those parts of nuclear physics that are studied primarily to elucidate the origin of the elements rather than the structure of the nucleus would, in my usage, be termed extrinsically motivated. On the other hand, the study of elementary particles, originally motivated by our desire to understand the nuclear force, now develops with a logic and urgency of its own dictated by the intrinsic interest and beauty of the phenomena occurring at very high energy. I would therefore call elementary particle physics pure. Of course, it is in the nature of pure science that the light it eventually will shed on other branches of science or technology is to some degree unpredictable; yet at any given time I believe one can often make a judgment of relevance on the basis of the motivation of those practicing the science. Thus, many nuclear physicists who measure capture cross sections make no bones about their primary motivation—it is to help the astrophysicist understand stellar nucleosynthesis better, rather than to help themselves understand the nucleus better.

At its inception nearly every science is extrinsically motivated—that is, it seeks to explain questions that were originally part of some other branch of human interest, usually, though by no means always, some practical matter. Mathematics originated because man had to measure, weigh, and count to maintain an organized economic order. The study of thermodynamics started from Carnot's interest in steam engines. Pasteur's science of bacteriology began when he tried to prevent the French beer and wine manufacturers' products from turning sour. Group theory was invented by Galois as a means of studying the properties of algebraic equations. So to speak, nearly every pure science starts as an applied or, at least, as an extrinsically motivated science.

And, indeed, in previous generations the distinction between pure and applied science was less pronounced than it is today. The three greatest pure mathematicians—Archimedes, Newton, and Gauss— were also great applied mathematicians; to these one can add the three greatest pure mathematicians of the twentieth century— Poincaré, Hilbert, and von Neumann—each of whom was great also as an applied mathematician. Pasteur, the founder of bacteriology, was an applied scientist. Lord Kelvin was equally at home in applied and in basic physics. Similarly, the distinction between theoretical and experimental science was much less sharp two generations ago than it now is. Maxwell did experiments as well as construct theories.

But daughter sciences, once they bud off the stalk of the parent science, acquire a separate existence, grow, and luxuriate. In the process these offspring generally become purer and narrower. The parent stalk had closer roots in the original questions posed by some urgent need: in chemistry, the need to extract metals or to find the elixir of life; in mechanics, to build more accurate missiles; in astronomy, to predict the seasons. But, today, more pressures compel the daughter science to become purer, especially when the science is pursued within the university.

To understand how this comes about, I remind you that every scientist or, for that matter, any intellectual creator, in plying his trade, tries to choose for himself problems that are both soluble and important. The importance of a problem is judged, by the scientist, by the breadth of the added understanding that its solution affords. The discovery of the second law of thermodynamics was important because it organized so many otherwise disjointed elements of physics and chemistry. Its discovery was much more important than, say, the discovery that light reflected at the Brewster angle is completely polarized, since the latter discovery affects a much narrower segment of related science or technology. The important questions often tend to be posed as much from without as from within a given narrow field of inquiry. The solution of an important problem tends to reinforce the relation between a scientific discipline and the neighboring disciplines to which it is related. In this sense, the important questions are broad—they tend to be extrinsically motivated.

Unfortunately, the important questions are often the most intractable ones, and therefore most of science is concerned with soluble problems, not important problems. We do not know how to create a controlled thermonuclear plasma; we therefore study aspects of plasmas that are tractable rather than necessarily relevant in the hope that our added general knowledge will eventually help us make progress toward the goal of controlled fusion. But in the process the science of plasma physics becomes "purer."

So, in general, the strategy of pure science is always to deal with soluble problems which, by their nature, tend to be narrow in impact. The important problems are skirted until enough soluble problems have been solved to permit a successful attack on the important problems. The social structure and purpose of the university accentuates the pressure toward purity. For the university's purpose is not to solve problems that are set from outside a discipline. The university is not mission-oriented. Its purpose is to create and encourage the intellectual life per se. If a scientific discipline sets off on an independent course, separate from its original applied parent, it tends, in the university, toward greater purity and remoteness simply because there are few countervailing pressures there. In the university it is improper to ask of the scientist: "What is the relevance of what you are doing to the rest of the world or even to the rest of science?" The acceptable question is: "What do your scientific peers, who view your work with the same intellectual prejudices as you, think of your work?"

The process leading toward greater purity and remoteness was described with exquisite perception by John von Neumann, though it had been discussed previously by Felix Klein and David Hilbert.[2] Speaking of the development of mathematics, von Neumann put it:

As a mathematical discipline travels from its empirical source, or still more, if it is a second and third generation only indirectly inspired from "reality" it is beset with very grave dangers. It becomes more and more

[2] Von D. Hilbert, "Mathematische Probleme," in *A Collection of Modern Mathematical Classics: Analysis,* Richard Bellman, ed. (New York, Dover, 1961). See Hilbert's lecture before the Mathematical Congress, Paris, 1900: "In the meantime, while the generating force of the pure thought acts, the external world enters again and again; it forces upon us new questions through the actual phenomena; it opens new topics of mathematics, and while we try to incorporate these new topics into the realm of pure thought, we find often the answers to old unsolved problems, and advance this way best the old theories. Upon this repeating and changing interplay between thought and experience are based, as it seems to me, the many and surprising analogies and that apparently 'prestabilized harmony' which the mathematicians so often notice in the questions, methods, and concepts of different fields of science."

pure aestheticizing, more and more purely *l'art pour l'art*. This need not be bad if the field is surrounded by correlated subjects, which still have closer empirical connections, or if the discipline is under the influence of men with exceptionally well-developed taste. But there is a grave danger that the subject will develop along the line of least resistance, that the stream so far from its source will separate into a multitude of insignificant branches, and that the discipline will become a disorganized mass of details and complexities. In other words, at a great distance from its empirical source, or after much abstract inbreeding, a mathematical subject is in danger of degeneration. At the inception the style is usually classical; when it shows signs of becoming baroque, then the danger signal is up. . . .

Whenever this stage is reached, the only remedy seems to me to be the rejuvenating return to the source: the reinjection of more or less directly empirical ideas. I am convinced that this was a necessary condition to conserve the freshness and vitality of the subject and that this will remain equally true in the future.[3]

Von Neumann's plea for greater unity in the mathematical sciences has been taken up by others, notably Mark Kac and Richard Courant, who see grave danger in the present trend toward super-purity, abstractness, and remoteness. Kac speaks of the professional purist in mathematics; Courant speaks of the "isolation that threatens every pursuit of science—certainly very much the pursuit of mathematics —this isolation can be very stifling." The trend toward isolation that has marked modern mathematics seems to me to have invaded the empirical sciences, and possibly even the social sciences, and for the same reasons. For example, the nuclear structure physicist today concerns himself with subtler, more delicate questions about nuclear structure than he did twenty years ago. And just because the questions are subtler, and more detailed, they tend to have less relevance to the fields of science and technology that surround nuclear structure physics. The language of the nuclear structure physicist becomes more sophisticated, his techniques more specialized. His ability to communicate with his colleagues in surrounding fields becomes impaired; and, in so far as what he studies becomes of less relevance to the fields in which his own field is embedded, his own field becomes purer.

[3] J. von Neumann, "The Mathematician," in *The Works of the Mind*, R. B. Heywood, ed. (Chicago, University of Chicago Press, 1947), p. 196.

THE DENIAL OF SCIENCE AS CODIFIER

The other major danger that I see in the development of science in the university is the tendency to downgrade science's role as codifier of human knowledge. Science traditionally has two aspects: it is, on the one hand, a technique for acquiring new knowledge; it is, on the other hand, a means for organizing and codifying existing knowledge, and therefore a tool for application. Both aspects of science are valid. The discovery of SU_3 symmetry does not in the slightest detract from the importance of the second law of thermodynamics. This law, with its enormous power as an organizing principle for much of existing chemistry, though discovered more than a century ago, is as much "science" as the *search* for new unitary symmetries.

The modern university tends to emphasize science as search at the expense of science as codification, and for many of the same reasons that it drives science toward fragmentation and purity. The codified parts of science are often most useful in the neighboring sciences, not in the science in which the codification originally took place. X-ray crystal analysis sprang up in physics; most X-ray crystallographers nowadays work as chemists, metallurgists, or even biologists. Thus the university's disciplinarity, its tendency to deal with pure problems that are intrinsically motivated, reduces its concern for science as codification; such science has already been by-passed by the researcher in the field.

The pressure to do research rather than teach accentuates the denial of science as codification. Much has been said about the conflict between research and teaching in the university. As I see it, at least part of the conflict amounts to a philosophic judgment as to whether science is the search for knowledge or the organizer of existing knowledge. In emphasizing research at the expense of teaching one is implicitly valuing the one above the other.

One by-product of this trend is the waning of the tradition of scientific scholarship. As our sciences become more and more fragmented and narrowly specialized and as their connection with earlier, more general phases of science weakens, the relevance of what came before for the pursuit of current research decreases. For example, it is possible to carry out research on elementary particles without knowing much about nuclear structure. The taste for knowing the historical origin and logical development of a science wanes—partly because such knowledge is unnecessary for prosecuting the current research, partly because there is too little time and energy left over after learning what is needed to do the research at hand.

IMPLICATIONS: FOR EDUCATION

These two tendencies—toward purity and fragmentation as opposed to application and interdisciplinarity, and toward research and away from scholarship—seem to me to portend trouble in the relation between the university and society.

First, I speak about the great curriculum reforms, especially in the sciences. These reforms started in the high schools but have now been extended, particularly in mathematics downward to the grade schools and, in many instances, upward to the colleges. They are relevant to my discussion since the reforms have been instigated by the university, and they certainly reflect the intellectual spirit of the university. With certain of the aims of the curriculum reform, one can have no quarrel. The new curricula try hard to be interesting, and in this I think they succeed; also, they demand more effort and present more challenge than the old. But in so far as some of the new curricula have been captured by university scientists and mathematicians of narrowly puristic outlook, in so far as the curricula reflect the deplorable fragmentation and abstraction, especially of mathematics, in so far as the curricula deny science as codification in favor of science as search, I consider them to be dangerous.

The danger I worry about was brought home to me by a distinguished physics professor. According to him, the mathematics department at his university no longer teaches the kind of calculus course that develops power and skill in handling simple integration. Such matters are apparently too low-brow and, in any event, are no longer needed by one who wishes to pursue a career as a research mathematician. As a result, many physics students are unable to do the mathematics that still is important for physics, even if not for mathematics. This physics professor has therefore written a book on calculus that presents the traditional parts of the subject that have been by-passed by the professionals. I think this anecdote illustrates both what is wrong with and what might be done to remedy the situation. The professional purists, representing the spirit of the fragmented, research-oriented university, got hold of the curriculum reform and, by their diligence and aggressiveness, have created puristic monsters. But education at the elementary level of a field is too important to be left entirely to the professionals in that field, especially if the professionals are themselves too narrowly specialized in outlook. Instead, curriculum reform should be strongly influenced by disciplines bordering the discipline being reformed. The mathematics curriculum should receive strong cues from the empirical sciences and from engineering; the physics curriculum, from engineering as well as from the neighboring sciences; and so on. There is nothing wrong with physics professors writing calculus books or engineering professors writing physics texts, as long as the physics professor knows calculus or the engineering professor knows physics. And, indeed, seeds of the counterrevolution in curriculum reform seem to be sprouting. In physics a group at Harvard under Gerald Holton is trying to devise a curriculum that views physics as a more broadly cultural activity than some of the other curricula. In mathematics a counterrevolution also seems to be taking place; for example, a group of seventy-five leading American mathematicians stated: "To offer such subjects to all students as could interest only the small minority of prospective mathematicians is wasteful and amounts to ignoring the needs of the scientific community and of society as a whole." [4] And the American Council for Curricular Evaluation has been organized to maintain "the intellectual integrity of our schools"—that is, to scrutinize some of our newer curriculum reforms.

Related to the trend toward purity in curriculum reform is the relatively poor place of applied science in the universities. This matter has been emphasized by Edward Teller.[5] He points out that most of the money our government spends for research and development goes

[4] L. V. Ahlfors, and others, "Mathematics Curriculum of the High School," *American Mathematical Monthly,* 69 (1962), 189–93.

[5] See for example, Teller's paper in "Basic Research and National Goals," a Report to the House Committee on Science and Astronautics, submitted by the National Academy of Sciences (March, 1965), pp. 257–66.

for applied research; yet most of the prestige and emphasis in the university goes to basic science. The best scientific minds go into basic, not applied, science; and the social hierarchy of science, reflecting the discipline-orientation of the university as much as it does the intrinsic logic of the situation, places pure science above the interdisciplinary applied science. Hans Bethe, in speaking of the social responsibility of the scientist, has also noted this denigration of the applied sciences in the university. He exhorts the university scientist to overcome his prejudice against application and especially urges him, as part of his social responsibility, to reaffirm the dignity of applied science.[6]

IMPLICATIONS: FOR GOVERNMENT

What are the implications of these trends for government and society? Our society increasingly is a product of the university. As the university degree becomes more and more common—it may be nearly as common, eventually, as a high school diploma is now—the outlook and point of view of our society and of our government becomes the outlook and point of view of the university.

I want to make perfectly clear that on balance I believe this to be enormously good. The university is rational, and its outlook is basically tolerant and knowledgeable. For example, I believe our whole enlightenment in race relations would have been unthinkable if anthropological and psychological doctrines, largely developed in the university, had not penetrated society as a whole. One must never forget that the Supreme Court, in justifying its 1954 decision on school desegregation, invoked a psychological doctrine (psychic trauma to the segregated child) that catches the spirit of and was certainly nurtured by the university.

But my purpose is to point out the dangers to government, to society, and to the university that lie in the latter's narrow disciplinarity. Thus the university's picture of science as research and denial of science as codification or as a tool deadens its taste for action. Let me illustrate with the report "Growth of World Population," released by the National Academy of Sciences in 1963 and to which I sub-

[6] "The Social Responsibilities of Scientists and Engineers," a lecture at Cornell University, November 6, 1963, published subsequently in *The Cornell Engineer* and excerpted in *SSRS Newsletter* (Gambier, Ohio), February, 1964, p. 1.

scribed at the time.[7] The report concluded that the over-all task was to achieve "universal acceptance of the desirability of planning and controlling family size." The report then made four major recommendations, which I paraphrase: (1) support graduate and postdoctoral training in demography; (2) expand research laboratories for scientific investigation of human reproduction; (3) cooperate in international studies of voluntary fertility regulation; (4) train more administrators of family planning.

With none of these recommendations can anyone concerned with the population problem take issue. Of course, we need more research and more studies, as well as more administrators. But such recommendations are, it now seems to me, tangential to the main issue. They substitute research about the problem of family planning for action on the problem. Complicated social problems such as control of family planning must be attacked with the information at hand even as we learn more about them. And, indeed, the distinguished biochemist, William D. McElroy, who chaired the panel that issued the report, said recently: "Although I am still in full agreement with these recommendations, I think the time has come when we must move ahead even without the additional biological knowledge." [8]

Nor is this incident an isolated one. Panels that advise government, especially on matters having scientific implications (and what affair of government these days does not?), are usually dominated by university people, especially those active in research. What is more natural than to recommend more research as a kind of magical talisman that will solve profound and complex social problems? I was, therefore, much impressed with the contrast between the recent study on heart, cancer, and stroke, which proposed specific concrete action on the basis of the knowledge at hand, and the many other studies, such as the National Academy of Sciences study on population, which display an inclination to study rather than to do.

Even the choice of what things our government decides to spend its

[7] National Academy of Sciences, Washington, D.C. Committee on Science and Public Policy, *The Growth of World Population* (Washington, D.C., National Research Council, 1963).

[8] "The Need for Action," in *Population,* panel discussion held at the Pan American Union (New York, Planned Parenthood—World Population, 1964), p. 43.

research funds on is now deeply influenced by the puristic university. In earlier, and simpler, times the government's attitude toward science was unsophisticated and inexpensive. First, the nonscientific goals of the society were ascertained by the political process; these goals by and large transcended the goals of the university. Thus, we had long since decided that national defense was a necessary goal; or good public health; or better navigation; or adequate physical and chemical standards. We then decided to support the science that scientists believed would help achieve these goals. How much we spent on the relevant science was determined by how important we regarded the goals themselves to be, and this was a political decision. It is true that in recent years we have become very relaxed over how relevant a science need be to warrant support; nevertheless, the mission-oriented agencies support basic science per se largely as a justified overhead expense charged against achievement of the over-all mission. Just as a good applied laboratory does a fair amount of related basic science, so an enlightened government agency supports a large amount of related basic research. But the ultimate justification of this basic research, as far as society at large is concerned, was the achievement of some nonscientific goal. If one examines the original basis for establishing the National Science Foundation, one finds that an eventual tangible and palpable pay-off of science was strongly in the minds of those who conceived the NSF.

The current active debate on scientific priorities bespeaks a change in our viewpoint. Whereas in previous times government support of science was justified by its contribution to the achievement of some nonscientific end, we seem now to have accepted the view that science deserves large support solely for its own sake; with this development no scientist can quarrel. However, to my mind, the same professionally puristic viewpoint that has captured the elementary mathematics curriculum seems to be prevailing in the present debate on scientific priority. The debate at the moment centers on the support given to high-energy physics relative to that given other fields of science. Now, high-energy physics is at once the most elegant and, in a sense, the most fascinating branch of physics. The new unitary symmetries are beautiful to behold and astonishingly unexpected. The high-energy physicists themselves are brilliant and dedicated. Because the field is rich and exciting in itself it certainly deserves support. I cannot, however, understand the argument that high-energy physics commands an *urgency* of support simply because, as Robert Oppenheimer puts it, it is "the conviction of those who are in it that, without further penetration into the realm of the very small, the agony may this time not end in a triumph of human reason." [9] The agony Oppenheimer refers to is surely not shared by all of society, nor even by all scientists. The question is why the intellectual agony of this generation of physicists needs to be relieved as quickly as possible rather than being resolved, at a slower pace, by succeeding generations.

To me urgent support of a field is justified only if that field is likely in some way to solve a pressing human need. The biomedical sciences merit urgent support because out of them come means of alleviating some of man's most primitive suffering—illness and premature death. The social sciences would merit urgent support in so far as they are aimed at helping solve man's social problems; unfortunately, in my opinion, they do not at this time seem ripe for great expansion. By contrast, high-energy physics offers little prospect of satisfying any *urgent* human need.

The emergence of high-energy physics among our country's highest-priority basic scientific enterprises is a manifestation both of the university's deification of purity in science and of its influence on what our society does. High-energy physics is the purest branch of physics. In the university community it towers above most sciences in prestige and in the caliber of the students it attracts. That it should be placed so high on our society's list of things to be done attests at once to the pervasiveness of the university's influence on the society and to the way in which fragmentation and concern for disciplinary purity of the university, when imposed on the mission-oriented society, diverts the society from its real goals. Our society is not a university; the goals of our society are not the same as the goals of the fragmented and discipline-oriented university. For the university to persuade the society that at this stage in history the university's own intellectual goals and aspirations—remote, pure, and fragmented—deserve the highest place among the goals of the society is hardly tenable.

[9] J. R. Oppenheimer, in *Nature of Matter,* Luke C. L. Yuan, ed. (Upton, N.Y., Brookhaven National Laboratory, 1965), p. 5.

RECAPITULATION: THE IMBEDDEDNESS OF VALUES

My remarks have been a fugue on a single theme. I began by pointing out that the university and society were incongruent in that the university was discipline-oriented and fragmented, the society mission-oriented and whole. I tried to show how the ecology of the discipline-oriented university encourages the rise of purism and specialization and the denial of scholarship and application in science. I then argued that these trends in the universities are affecting our elementary curricula, giving us poorer people to get on with the applied work of the day, substituting research for action, and tending to impose the scientific values of the fragmented university upon the society.

In every one of these trends I discern the same underlying issue: a failure to realize that no judgment of relative value of a universe can be made from the narrow base of that universe. Values are established from without a universe of discourse; means are established from within. Thus, our science tends to become more fragmented and more narrowly puristic because its practitioners, harried as they are by the social pressures of the university community, have little time or inclination to view what they do from a universe other than their own. They impose upon the elementary curricula their narrowly disciplinary point of view, which places greater value on the frontiers of a field than on its tradition, and they try to put across what seems important to them, not what is important when viewed in a larger perspective. The practitioners have no taste for application nor even for interdisciplinarity since this takes them away from their own universe; and they naturally and honestly try to impose their style and their standards of value upon society, as when they insist on research instead of action or when they claim urgency for matters whose urgency—that is, whose importance—is largely self-generated.

For the universities, and for the members of the universities, I have some recommendations although I put them forward diffidently. The university must restore to the specialist of broader outlook the status and prestige it now confers solely upon the specialist of narrow outlook. Granted that specialization is "blessed" in the sense that only the specialist knows what he is talking about; yet, if only the specialist knows what he is talking about, only the generalist knows why he should talk at all.

Can the university combine the point of view of the specialist with that of the generalist? Can it acquire some of the mission-orientation of the large laboratory, yet retain its discipline-orientation intact? Can it truly become interdisciplinary and whole, and thus become once more congruent with society?

Several possibilities suggest themselves, though I do not pretend that these possibilities are panaceas. The university could convert itself into the National Laboratory. This is surely going too far, even though mission-oriented institutes are springing up on university campuses, largely, I believe, in response to the contradictions that I have outlined. The university certainly should not give up the freedom and the individual autonomy of the professor—the freedom and autonomy he cannot enjoy when he enters the mission-oriented institute. Thus, much as I approve of the mission-oriented institute, I value the professor's stubborn freedom even more, and so I would hate to see the university become the National Laboratory.

I would go farther. Many of the shortcomings I find in the university are intrinsic characteristics of the university and are hardly susceptible to change. The university loses something unique and precious when it submerges the professor's independence to achieve a common scientific mission conceived by administrators. But this means, simply, that some things are not properly done at the university. For example, the important problems even in pure science that transcend in difficulty the capacity and style of the university, like studies of genetics involving 200,000 mice, or modern plasma physics, must be done outside the university. Moreover, the basic research that goes to support such activities is properly the business of institutions having such responsibilities. Thus my plea amounts to reasserting the validity of the National Laboratory, with its shortcomings that I know so well, as a home for certain kinds of basic and applied research, even as I emphasize the place of the university, with its shortcomings, in the scientific society. The view that federal support of basic research is the university's inalienable right and that, if competition with the mission-oriented institutions arises, then the university's is the prior claim (as suggested in the recent Wooldridge report on NIH) [10] to my mind ignores the shortcomings of the university in basic research. There is an appropriate analogy here between the two kinds of institutions: the university and the mission-oriented laboratory. Basic research is supported in the mission-oriented laboratory to help the laboratory accomplish its mission. As Harvey Brooks has suggested,[11] it ought to be looked upon as a reward for achievement of the laboratory's mission, especially since the basic researcher is thereby given a stake in achievement of the laboratory's mission. Similarly, a case can be made for giving the university, as an institution, support for basic research, as a reward for excellence in teaching, since thereby one gives to the research professor a stake in the university's mission.

For, in a sense, the university, no less than the laboratory is already mission-oriented if only it will accept and recognize its traditional mission—education of the young. And just as the mission-orientation of the National Laboratory adds point and wholeness to its scientific activity, so pregraduate education ought to give wholeness to the university. Education at the undergraduate level should properly be less professionalized and puristic than it is at the highest levels. Just as ontogeny recapitulates phylogeny, so elementary education properly should recapitulate the historic path of a discipline: its connections with other disciplines and with practical purposes, its origin, its scholarship—in short, its place in the scheme of things. If the university takes undergraduate education seriously and does not look upon it simply as attenuated professional education, the university community will be forced to broaden its outlook. The university professor would, by enforced contacts with young people whose backgrounds are diverse, surely be obliged to relate his narrow professional interest to the rest of the world. And in the process, as he becomes part of the interdisciplinary real world, the teacher ought once more to become a citizen.

[10] *Biomedical Science and Its Administration, A Study of the National Institutes of Health, Report to the President,* D. E. Wooldridge, Chairman (Washington, D.C., U.S. Government Printing Office, 1965).

[11] In the report, "Basic Research and National Goals," a Report to the House Committee on Science and Astronautics, submitted by the National Academy of Sciences, March, 1965, pp. 77–110.

Leland J. Haworth

A NEW CALL FOR EXCELLENCE IN AMERICAN UNIVERSITIES

We Americans are known for our love of football and hamburgers, comic strips and automobiles, chewing gum and hi-fi. But our most steadfast, most enduring national romance is our love affair with education. Americans in all walks of life and in all sections of the country—though frequently at odds with one another on political, social, economic, and other matters—are in general agreed on these propositions: education is a good thing; it has been good for our country; it is important to us all; and it will be even more crucial to our welfare and progress in the future.

It has been thus since our earliest beginnings. I wonder how many of you have ever read "The Hoosier Schoolmaster," the story of a frontier teacher; it has been nearly fifty years since I have done so. But I still recall the drama of one climactic scene. It concerned a spelling bee, an event of compelling interest to the entire community, partaken in by youngsters and adults alike. The climax occurred when all had been eliminated but the schoolmaster and a country girl named Hannah, for whom, if memory serves me right, the schoolmaster had developed an affection. Excitement grew as each correctly met the successive challenges. Finally he stumbled on a word—I do not remember what—"And Hannah spelled it right." She was a heroine to all.

These pioneer folk had a deep respect for learning for its own sake. For most, it had little or nothing to do with livelihood. To clear the forests and till the soil, to hunt and trap, to cook and wash, to spin and weave and sew—these things were learned by experience and by the example of one's elders; the skills developed were taken for granted, though respected. But "book larnin'" was something else again. There was a deep yearning to partake in the joys of intellectual experience, however limited. Reverence for the schoolmaster was exceeded only by that accorded to the preacher, who was also, at least relatively, a man of learning. There was an abiding respect for those who could excel, as Hannah did.

Purdue University is in itself a forceful reminder of this longstanding interest of our people. It is well endowed with the three basic elements that constitute a university—an eager and intelligent student body, a faculty of able and dedicated scholars, and an imposing array of academic facilities. To be sure, it is not typical of our institutions of higher learning, for Purdue is much larger and better equipped than most. In keeping with their traditions, the citizens of Indiana have been generous in their support of this and their other colleges and universities. Indeed few institutions anywhere can match, in scale or completeness, the academic facilities at Purdue. Nevertheless, as I visit campuses across the country, I am continually impressed by the educational plants I see. These are the outward evidences of our common inner conviction that education is of primary importance and must be given more and more support.

There are those who maintain that a great teacher will attract dedicated students regardless of the environment or the nature of facilities available. Unquestionably, there is some support for this opinion in the history of education. There was Mark Hopkins on a log. There were the great European teachers of the past such as Peter Abélard of Paris, whose students, attracted from all over Europe, sat for hours at a stretch on a straw-littered floor, taking notes on waxed tablets placed upon an uplifted knee.

But as the nature of society has changed, so have the meaning and the purpose of higher education. It is no longer sufficient for the educator to convey a definitive body of knowledge to the student, like a blood transfusion or like pouring so much grain into a silo. A modern institution of higher education must instead expose the student to a spectrum of intellectual, emotional, and social experiences to which he will react beneficially. The educator scatters grain on the fertile soil of youthful intellect and imagination. He nourishes it with the rain of inspiration, and the harvest is the unfolding of the student.

This, together with the nature of much of modern knowledge, requires that the educational setting have available not merely space in which to live and work but also a vast array of tools with which to work—books and journals, laboratory equipment and supplies, greenhouses and controlled environment chambers.

Moreover, the modern university has become not just a place where knowledge is dispensed but, more and more, a place where knowledge is originated. It is a center for research in both the natural and the social sciences and for the equivalent pursuit of knowledge or creativity in all the other fields. Especially at the graduate level, such activities commingle with—indeed are hardly distinguishable from—education. But again, they require tools.

Thus we see the importance of the balance between the basic essential elements of a university. Is the student body worthy of the talents and dedication of the faculty? Is the faculty, in turn, worthy of the students, and of the responsibility to increase our intellectual heritage? Are the physical facilities adequate to fill the requirements of both groups? When we consider how difficult it is to assemble on one site these ingredients, each of which is essential to quality in higher education, we may well marvel at the fact that we have done as well as we have.

Let me make it clear at once that I am among those who believe that we *have* done well. American higher education—and our educational structure at all other levels—is increasingly being examined by people in all parts of the world as they consider their own educational plans for the future. I think we should take it as a compliment that the countries of Europe are more and more looking toward these shores for ideas relevant to the ways in which they may go about rethinking their own educational systems. Traditionally, the quality of education in several of the major European nations has been thought of throughout the world as the standard of excellence to which one compared all other educational systems. Until the relatively recent past, American universities were seldom seriously considered as competitive with the universities of Germany, France, and the United Kingdom in so far as providing doctorate training in the more advanced fields of science was concerned. But nowadays we can as-

suredly compare our doctoral graduates with those from the more ancient universities of Western Europe without feeling the sense of
inferiority that long marked our view of our own graduate institutions.

Having said this, however, it is important also to note that the very
nature of the evolution of American education has led to a different
kind of educational philosophy from that which has characterized the
educational systems in Western Europe. Our goal of providing education for the children of all our people has already led us to a position
which many other countries have in the past considered themselves
unable to reach.

In recent years this has become a concerted national goal. President Johnson is one of the most earnest advocates. Make no mistake
about it, he is deadly earnest when he expresses the desire to see provided for each youngster in the land the most extensive and highest
quality educational opportunity that youngster is capable of using. I
have heard him say so in no uncertain terms to small groups, under
circumstances that reveal great depth of feeling in these matters. He
considers education to be the most important cornerstone of any
great society, and he watched the passage of his education bills with
great interest and satisfaction.

The title of this paper is "A New Call for Excellence in American
Universities." The "new call" in my subject is not, as may have been
suspected from the nature of this volume, an exhortation for more
and better research results. But rather it is one that has been sounded
by the American people, first by a greatly increased desire to improve the quality of education at all levels, and then by providing
bumper crops of students for our universities and colleges. At no
time in our history have we faced the prospect that we must now consider—that of providing in one decade an additional number of classrooms, laboratories, library facilities, faculty members, and other
constituents of a higher educational system that would virtually equal
in size, complexity, and costliness the entire higher educational system of the United States in 1960.

The new call, therefore, is a call to assure continued qualitative
improvements in our university-level education for all students in the
face of the very large numbers of students who are already beginning

to swell the college population. In the fall of 1963 the number of first-time enrollments in American colleges and universities exceeded the number in the preceding year by 1.6 percent; the rise in the fall of 1964 over the fall of 1963 was a startling 17 percent. We know from the numbers of young people in the age group that will provide the majority of college freshmen in September, 1965, that we may expect still another abrupt rise at that time. Moreover, we are still observing a gradual rise in the fraction of each age group which enters and graduates from college. When one looks at these problems in combination, it is easy to see that the situation we face is indeed a difficult one.

These are not new or newly perceived problems. Years ago those who make predictions about college enrollments foresaw the present situation. The phrase "the tidal wave of college students" was coined before 1960. But, at the meeting of the American Council on Education in the fall of 1964, various speakers pointed to the fact that, despite all warnings, there has been an inadequate response. Hence there are many ways in which our institutions of higher education are falling short of making adequate provision for the young people who are now ready for and, in many instances, entering upon college study. There are few institutions where the requisite amount of preparation for the "tidal wave" has been made; therefore we now see emergency provisions being invented and used on many campuses to provide for the rapidly rising enrollments.

Because we have tried to do so much in the field of education, we have set for ourselves a difficult problem. We have found it hard enough to improve quality even when the rate of growth in our educational institutions is about the same as that of the population as a whole or of the Gross National Product. In fact, however, we are in a situation where we must provide for a much more rapid enlargement of our educational system than for the rate of growth of the economy, for the rate of growth of the labor force, or for any of the other ordinary measures of this kind. If we were to decide that we could do no more than maintain the level of quality in higher education that we have already achieved, we would be forced to make efforts well above the levels of the past. But this is not enough. Our aspirations are and must remain higher.

It is on this responsibility that I intend to focus my subsequent remarks, for it is the universities that must take the leadership in our whole education process. They must help the colleges as well as help themselves to educate the future generations of college students. And both must do their utmost to help assure high quality educational opportunities for the oncoming pre-college students. By this I do not belittle the role of the universities as producers of new knowledge for its own sake. I have made many speeches on the importance of that role. But now I wish to dwell upon the immediately pressing challenge, even in academic research, to focus attention on developing to the utmost the talents of the throngs of eager, able youngsters who are pounding on the doors of the undergraduate colleges and soon will do so at the graduate school level.

Let us think for a moment about some of the reasons why we consider it so important to educate our young people. There are, of course, many and varied reasons that can be given. I call your attention to several, with no particular order of priority.

First, we need to develop more scholars—individuals who value, preserve, impart to others, and (frequently but not always) add to the store of knowledge in a field of intellectual substance.

Second, we need to provide the members of each new generation the knowledge, the skill, the intellectual tools required to carry out the specific tasks society needs to have accomplished and, at the same time, to enable them to earn a livelihood.

Third, we need to make sure that those who emerge from the educational system carry with them into adult life a set of attitudes and values that, combined with their more detailed or specialized knowledge, will enable them to play their part as responsible citizens in a general sense.

Finally, and importantly, we need to see to it that each new generation has the opportunity of tasting the joys and feeling the inspiration that can come from a stimulating exposure to mankind's cultural heritage. For the greatest human triumphs and the greatest human joys are of the mind and spirit.

I realize fully that these reasons for educating the young are interconnected in several important ways. But for my purposes, this listing will suffice. What I want to demonstrate, simply stated, is that our colleges and universities must of necessity serve a broad set of purposes.

Let us look, in the context of these purposes, at the three essential elements mentioned earlier—students, faculty, and material resources. Certainly there is no dearth of students; indeed their very numbers have intensified the task. Our problems lie in the last two.

In principle there should be no lasting problem of material resources. Surely this wealthy nation can afford everything that is required. All that is needed is the informed will of the people, acting through the various levels of government and through private organizations. And, adequately provided, such resources could be quickly brought to bear on our needs. The most vexing problem is the need to educate adequately more qualified individuals to serve as teachers both in our educational system at all levels from nursery school through graduate school education and in the increasing numbers of "continuing education" centers that are proving to be most important as a means of producing such specialists as engineers, doctors, lawyers and other groups. And unfortunately all of this takes time as well as resources.

Having said that resources should not be a *lasting* problem, let me readily admit that they nevertheless present their own problems: How to assure their adequacy? how to use them wisely?

As to sources of support, the bulwark should continue to be nonfederal sources. Institutions fit themselves into their environment and flourish or decay depending on the degree to which they adjust to their environment and its particular demands. The American people have demanded many different things of the educational system that has grown up here within the last two centuries, and many special demands will continue to be placed upon the educational system by the localities, the states, and various special groups, both religious and secular, that provide support for certain educational components. This is as it should be in our pluralistic society. We do not want a system of education that relies upon central authority for its major support and guidance. The variety of institutions that we now have at the higher education level—and at lower levels as well—and the many different ways in which these educational entities receive their support guarantee a kind of freedom of action that is essential to the preservation of educational integrity. Moreover, this diversity provides assurance that there will be little "hardening of the arteries" of these institutions, because there is always the spur and the challenge of competition provided by the distinctive characteristics of the nearby school or college or university.

Nevertheless, substantial federal support is needed for many purposes. A preponderant fraction of the federal money that has gone into the universities since 1945 has been for scientific research. Many of us are convinced that this has been a good investment—but that we now must consider other mechanisms for supplying assistance from the federal government for higher education. This new assistance, moreover, will have to be less research-oriented and more concerned with the combined teaching-research function of the college and university. We shall also probably have to look very carefully at the criteria being used and to be used to make sure that we are not denying opportunities for qualitative growth to certain colleges and universities by channeling available funds to those that already have achieved a substantial level of excellence, at least as measured according to the accepted criteria.

We must recall at all times that federal funds can appropriately be made available only for programs that afford essentially equal opportunity for all who are properly qualified and that promise benefits (directly or indirectly) for all. If, in a specific program, one sets about to identify and support individuals of great promise who are to perform work for the benefit of everyone, this is obviously one way of assuring benefits to all citizens without considering every American to be an equivalent applicant for such support. Thus, in many programs, we can be selective without becoming discriminatory. Even so, and especially when we come to deal with institutions rather than individuals, we must be extremely careful that we do not adopt criteria for support that become both selective and discriminatory.

Many of these points are well illustrated by the programs of support of academic science. Research at the frontiers of science is a costly business. Expensive equipment, quantities of consumable supplies, and adequte nonprofessional assistance are required. Universities simply could not afford it at anything like the present level without federal support. Such support has grown prodigiously, primarily to assure new scientific knowledge essential to pursuit of national goals in defense, in space, in health, in energy development, and so on. With this aim in mind, support has concentrated in those institutions where there exist the people most qualified to produce results. It has been selective without being discriminatory. Thus fewer than twenty universities receive half of the research support. They deserve and should continue to receive support, on an increasing scale. But this is not enough. We must, on an even greater relative scale, increase support of universities not now among the leaders, both to increase the direct scientific output and, what is more important, to enhance the education process. For both purposes we must develop more "centers of excellence."

As an aside, let me point out that in our discussions of institutional excellence there is too frequently a certain degree of semantic confusion, for excellence is, after all, a comparative word. Thus, unless we are comparing them with, for instance, those in the past or with institutions in other lands, to say that we now have and should continue to have excellent universities implies that we expect to have some that are not so good as the best. This, of course, will inescapably be true, but I believe we should be careful not to imply that we will be satisfied with some magic, relatively small number of institutions that excel, without at the same time being clear that we hope to raise all of our institutions to a high qualitative level as measured by absolute standards appropriate to their purposes.

This last is, of course, important in the general public interest. Many of our most gifted students are in other than our leading universities. Moreover, the American ethic has imbedded in it a strong commitment that everyone should receive equitable treatment; "fair play" is a hallmark of our entire society. I think we have not yet invoked this aspect of our heritage as fully as we might in pushing toward a higher standard of quality in our system of higher education.

None of this, of course, is meant to say that individual institutions should not strive to excel. Of course they should, for striving to excel is an important cause for progress in all human endeavors. But it *is* meant to say that the country as a whole should strive to help improve educational quality across the board.

Many federal programs are now directed at broadening the base of institutions of high quality in science. But even this process requires that the foremost continue to be supported and that their quality improve. For it is from them that will emerge a major fraction of the leaders who will help to elevate the others.

And this brings me to the faculties.

At a time many if not most of us can remember, nearly all of our colleges and universities were—and considered themselves to be—primarily instructional institutions. To be sure, there were some which were concerned with the advancement of knowledge as *one of* their major objectives. But even at such institutions, research was looked upon as somewhat subsidiary to the major function of imparting knowledge to students; and the "production" of well-educated graduates was considered both a necessary *and* a worthwhile goal. There were two varieties of scholarship that received essentially equal recognition. One type of scholar focused his efforts largely on the problem of keeping himself thoroughly informed of the latest as well as the older work in his field, and frequently contributed important analytical or expository monographs to the field, but engaged in relatively little or no original research—I shall refer to such individuals as "teacher-scholars"; the other type of scholar specialized more and carried out original work in his specialty that pushed forward his field of knowledge—such individuals I shall characterize as "research-scholars." Obviously, we now see more of this latter kind of scholar, especially in the sciences; I think it is fair to say, moreover, that research-scholars are nowadays more highly regarded than teacher-scholars.

All this is merely to say that, a few decades ago, research was considered something of a luxury, a desirable but not essential component of the college or university scene. On some campuses its value as an adjunct to the process of instruction was not well appreciated. The idea of a university serving as a major source of new knowledge has come a long way in the past fifty years in this country. There are some who now are warning us that the tail may be growing so big that it will soon wag the dog. I shall return to this matter again. I have already referred to the line of argument that convinces me that we must strive to move toward broadening the base of excellence. But we must be sure that we do not define too narrowly the criteria we use for assessing excellence.

Institutions that are clearly superior in their graduate programs and in related research *may* also fulfill their responsibilities in providing for the educational needs of their undergraduates in a comparably outstanding fashion. But we must not assume that these two related but distinct functions inevitably parallel one another in quality. Our top-flight liberal arts colleges do an excellent job of providing educational experiences for undergraduates. Their graduates compete without difficulty with the graduates of some of our noted multiversities (the term used by President Clark Kerr of the University of California). Some of the faculty members in the colleges that do a superior job along these lines are active in research, but others are more properly described as teacher-scholars. Hence it may not be so true as we have sometimes claimed that only the faculty member who is actively engaged in creative scholarship can do a good job as a teacher. I suspect that we could easily find many individuals who would stoutly maintain that only a good research-scholar can be a good university teacher. Certainly this is so at the graduate level. But at the undergraduate level I question this position. I hope it is not true, for it would not be feasible, at least now, to make real research centers out of all our colleges. In any case, I have no hesitation at all in saying that the converse is not always true; it simply is not so that all good research-scholars are good teachers. On balance I am inclined strongly to the belief that for some time past we have made a mistake in underrating the importance of what I have called the teacher-scholar. Of one thing I *am* sure: the good teacher must be a scholar. He must be passionately interested in and practice the intellectual process. He must continue to learn and to discover, for himself at least, even if he does not do so in the originating sense. This relates, I believe, to the most important shortcoming of the unfortunate over-emphasis on methodology that plagued pre-college education for so long. Inadequate attention in the teacher's training period on the subject matter he would teach resulted not only in inadequate knowledge for direct instructional purposes; even more importantly it allowed no opportunity to *appreciate* the subject—no chance to be a scholar.

According to any reasonable standard, we have today too few well-prepared and stimulating teachers at all educational levels. The situation may well become worse before it improves. In any case, however, the colleges and universities of this country have a special responsiblility to try to do the best job they can both in motivating able students toward careers in teaching and in making sure that the education these individuals receive fits them as fully as possible for the teaching roles they are to play. Since I am explicitly including junior college, senior college, and graduate faculty members in my term "teachers," and since much of the training of individuals for such jobs is carried out at the university level, I am specifically calling attention to the responsibility that our universities should respond to more fully, that of guiding a reasonable fraction of their graduates toward such careers.

In particular, those institutions that have already achieved eminence should avoid the point of view—one that I think is sometimes too easily accepted by many individuals—that the primary function of such institutions is to educate scholars who are upon graduation to move on to an institution of equal eminence to educate more scholars, some of whom then will return to the first-mentioned institution, whereupon the process would begin again. I think it is fair to say that the kind of parochialism that has led to and fed upon such "closed loop" arrangements is fading away; certainly our major institutions themselves are all recognizing and responding to their duties as national (and even international) educational resources. They most certainly should do so in all cases. I do not claim that federal support has in any given case been the primary factor that has led to pre-eminence—in science, where the major support has been provided, or in any other field. But all of our outstanding institutions have received large amounts of support, in various ways, from the national programs now growing apace. The institutions that receive substantial federal support have a special obligation to help repay society by helping other institutions to improve their quality.

In the specific case of colleges and universities that are still struggling to reach their own particular qualitative goals, a crucial problem has been and will remain that associated with the recruitment of well-qualified faculty members. I am convinced that our top-flight universities—and the individuals comprising their faculties—are going to have to consider even more carefully in the future than in the past the ways in which they can help to solve or ameliorate the problems being faced by what we may call the developing college or university.

And both must bear in mind, and more effectively discharge, their obligations to education at all levels. In this area of broad responsibility lies one of the greater challenges of the new call for excellence.

CONCLUSION: INTIMATIONS OF
THE FUTURE

Somebody suggested to me that in this summary I might feel able to give what you call guide lines. I want to assure you emphatically that I have no guide lines to give, particularly in the United States of America. When I go back to my own college, I shall sit in the old hall of Clare College and have dinner; and hanging over my table in the hall there are two portraits—one of Cornwallis and the other of the Duke of Newcastle. I suppose these are the two men who more than any others are responsible for Britain's losing the American colonies a hundred and ninety years ago. I therefore feel that you in America should regard Clare College as one of your great benefactors because, as far as I can see, you have got on pretty well in the last hundred and ninety years without any advice from the British. But, at any rate, with this background I do not propose to allow Clare College to exert any more influence upon the American people.

Nor am I going to summarize these excellent papers for three reasons: (1) It would take too long; (2) those who presented the papers presumably have given more attention to what they said than I have; and (3) I assume you are all intelligent enough to have understood them the first time. So I shall try to give briefly the sort of resonance that has arisen in my own mind from these papers. A resonator has to make clear what his *bona fides* are. I am someone from what Alvin Weinberg would call a chronically disciplined-oriented institution. It is said of Cambridge that you can always find somebody there who will produce a problem to any solution. And I hesitate, after all the questions that have been raised in these papers, to try to raise two or three more instead of giving solutions. But raising questions is, I am afraid, another chronic weakness of the university where I work. Somebody asked the difference between Oxford University and Cambridge. I can give you a very simple guide so that in the future it will not be necessary to ask the question again and so that it makes quite clear the virtues of Oxford. There was a civil service examination at which one of the questions was: "Write an essay on the medieval discussion about the number of angels which could be supported on the point of a pin." The Oxford candidate wrote a most delightful essay, charming, with all sorts of allusions from Medieval Latin, with reflections back to the Renaissance, with discussion of the views of the Church, and so on. The examiner was very puzzled to find that the answer from the Cambridge man covered only two lines, and they were these: "Before discussing this subject, I need to know three things, the diameter of the pin and the mass and specific gravity of the angels." That does summarize the difference in spirit between our two universities. With these warnings I shall come to the one or two points I should like to make.

The first one is this. I think that historically the problems of science and public policy are unique and without precedent. This is because of the gigantic size and the expense in manpower and money of modern scientific institutions. Seven hundred years ago, if a university became dissatisfied with its town-gown relations, the students and professors simply put their books on their backs and walked to the next town—the whole university would migrate. Even a hundred and fifty years ago, as Frederick Seitz reminded us in his paper (and I can confirm it even though it is about my own country), you could have closed every university in Great Britain, and it would have made no difference whatever to the progress of science. This new dilemma of size has appeared even within my lifetime. I think I belong to the first generation of scientists who have had to deal with scientific effort that is so expensive, capital investment in experiments that is so great, that universities sometimes find themselves designing professors to fit the apparatus instead of the other way around. One of the most exasperating consequences of size is the difficulty of liquidating an institution that has become worthless and has outlived its usefulness. Even with your courage, you have not learned how to do this yet in the

United States, and my own country is littered with institutions that are very interesting for the antiquarian but are no longer making very powerful contributions to knowledge. So this problem of size, this continually increasing critical mass, as it were, of scientific institutions is, I think, the chief cause of our difficulties. When institutions were small and when government's participation in them was only marginal, communication was easy and natural, almost as easy as the passage of ideas in the extended family of an African tribe. You only have to go back about fifty years to the time when, if you had a meeting of the British Association for the Advancement of Science, one hall could contain what Edward Teller called (rather invidiously) "everybody who is anybody in science," together with a number of key politicians and industrialists. Those were the times when our great statesmen like Balfour and Haldane would never miss a meeting of the British Association, and they met pretty well every working scientist in Britain on these occasions. And certainly within my lifetime, in a little country like ours with a comparatively small population of people doing research and organizing and financing science, most questions of policy could be settled informally, before anything was put on paper, by conversations in the corner of the Athenaeum Club in London.

All this has changed. Our anxieties now are not due to the inability of scientists to pursue good science nor to the inability of politicians to pursue politics. They are due to a silting-up of the channels of communication between scientists and politicians and administrators—between the man who pays the piper and the man who produces the tune. We know that, when Balfour was Foreign Secretary of Britain, he kept in close touch with the leaders of science; he knew what was going on in laboratories. The PH.D. in Britain, which was started in 1919, was established not on the initiative of the British universities; indeed at first they resisted it! It was established on the initiative of Balfour as Foreign Secretary. At the end of World War I he explained to Britain that, just as for the last fifty years preceding that time Americans had gone to Germany to get PH.D.s, we must now offer something to attract American research students to Britain. Our PH.D. was a device to produce, at any rate, a temporary brain drain in our direction across the Atlantic. Now, if what I have said is true, then I suppose the prime problem in formulating satisfactory equilibrium between scientists and their patrons, which is the basis of public policy in science, is to keep open these channels of communication. I think Harvey Brooks has summarized beautifully, in a way I had never thought of before, the double problem and the double traffic that has to go along these channels of communication, when he said that it is necessary not only to create and maintain a policy for science but also to use science for policy-making. Both these activities require easy communication between scientists and patrons. How is this to be assured?

Albert Crewe has said that the problem of science and public policy can be solved, or partly solved at any rate, under a great variety of social patterns. There have been successful equilibria established in this country by the contract system described by Donald Hornig; in my country by what I called *laissez-faire* government-sponsored patronage of science; and in the Soviet Union by the centralized planning system, which I also summarized in my paper. If it is true, and I believe it is, that one can get successful partial solutions to this problem under various social patterns, then obviously the question we have to ask is what is the common factor in these successful solutions for reaching a satisfactory equilibrium between science and public policy under various diverse patterns.

I think I have learned a possible half-answer from these papers. It is a biologist's answer. It is that when cells get too big they have to divide; it is physiologically impossible for a community to survive if it is too big. It is also psychologically impossible for a community to survive if it is too big. There has to be come subdivision into units comfortable enough for the human personality to stand. And so I believe that, in the dissemination of ideas in this cross-fertilization between politicians and scientists, between patron and university faculty, there is in fact no substitute for personal human relations and face-to-face exchange. Even modern technology, with all its incredible devices, has failed to provide any satisfactory substitute for personal relations. And so, in my view, the common factor in all successful equilibria between scientists and their patrons is really the division of institutions into small units, each of which has some responsibility and some authority and a clear channel of communication to representatives of the patrons. I was very impressed with what Frederick Seitz presented in his paper, because I am sure the real secret of the success of Office of Naval Research has been that the man with the ideas received the money direct and felt he had a personal contact between himself and a representative of what is vaguely called "the authorities." This personal relationship is the first requirement for setting up an equilibrium between the patron and the scientists, which is the basis of public policy in science. If you have done that, you have satisfied one of the conditions for solving the equation.

I can think of two other conditions. One of course—and it is really the most difficult one—is to provide cohesion between all these discrete and partly autonomous particles into which institutions are divided for good administration. Take one example. I regard the University of Cambridge, which is in some way a very successful university, as a constellation of anarchies. Each anarchy is, in fact, almost self-determining. Some of them are enormously successful, both as educational and as research units. What we fail to have at Cambridge is cohesion to hold the lot together. On this account the University of Cambridge is becoming almost incapable of making decisive corporate decisions. The whole university was divided in 1963 about whether there should be a comfort station outside the Botanic Garden. Even this is something on which no decision could be made administratively.

I have said that, if you have divided your big institutions into small units, you have satisfied one of the conditions for a satisfactory equilibrium between scientist and patron. What is the other? If the patron and the scientist, once you have brought them together, misunderstand one another and quarrel, quite clearly you have not solved the problem. How then do you maximize the chances of mutual understanding between patron and scientist? I think Beardsley Graham has given us a glimpse of the answer to this. I was fascinated by his statement that in the institute over which he presides a great deal of importance is attached to understanding human nature. He used the jargon "behavioral sciences," but what this really means is knowing what people are like, how they will react, what they think. This brings me then to my second point.

Have you ever thought that a scientist will go to great trouble to train himself, or to get assistants trained, to program computers, but only mechanical computers? Now politicians and administrators are walking computers. How much trouble do scientists take to program politicians and administrators? This is an art just as complicated as programming a large Atlas computer, and I do not know of any formal training given in this art in my country; and I imagine that even in your country formal training for programming administrators is not as good as it ought to be. There is another side to this, namely, that politicians and administrators have not learned how to program scientists either. I think if anything they are less good at it than we are at programming them, because we want to get money out of them and they do not quite know what they want to get out of us. So, in the end, I think the prospects of having a national policy for science and harnessing science for policy depend on something very simple, simply on one human being understanding another, persuading another, and trusting another.

If I have anything serious at all to say in this final summary, it is this: Having been on both sides of this fence, having been a research scientist for twenty years and an administrator for another fifteen, I believe very firmly that the understanding of human beings is not to be learned solely from books on psychology or from taking credit courses in public relations; I think it has to be learned from the humanities, from the liberal arts. My prescription, for instance, for an official at the Soviet desk in the State Department in Washington is not that he should have majored in international relations and economics; it is that he should have soaked in Tolstoy, Dostoevski, and Shakespeare's tragedies. When you come to think of it, the cold war, which we hope will be the only war in our lifetime, is being fought by graduates in the humanities; it is being fought by words and ideas about human beings. The experts in this field are not scientists and engineers; they are men who have specialized in words and ideas in relation to people. So I believe that the prerequisite for any solution of the problems raised in these papers is the capacity to understand and conduct private human relations. And so the study of individual man, the nurture of the humanities in our universities, not as a pseudoscience but as they were nurtured at the time of the Renaissance, is the key to forming contracts between the scientist and his patron. For although these arrangements may be made formally by signing a contract between Purdue University and the Office of Naval Research, in the end these contracts are really made between two individuals; the rest *is* just a formality that comes afterwards.

One of the side effects, I think, of size in our institutions is that people are quite rightly revolting against the concept of statistical man, against the idea that it is an institution that agrees with an institution rather than a man reaching an agreement with another man. I believe that this is a cause of the unrest among students, not only in your country but in mine. We have no Berkeley campus incident yet to focus our attention on the problem, but we do have similar phenomena—thousands of British students belonging to the campaign for Nuclear Disarmament, holding sit-ins in Trafalgar Square all night, some spending the night in jail and having to explain to me the next morning why they did not sleep in college. I believe that this and the Berkeley outbreak and other similar incidents are, in fact, merely a protest of the young that they are tired of being taught and administered by remote control. They want to meet and touch and talk to and argue with the people who really are supposed to be making contact with them. In our quite understandable preoccupation with the needs of science we are in danger of overlooking the needs of scientists. I remember Edward Teller once using the nice metaphor of a zoological garden of computers with trained animal keepers. I felt that he was a little bit too preoccupied with the computers and not quite enough with the animal keepers. We must not underestimate, in our enthusiasm about the capacity of computers, the importance and capacity of the human mind. I like to remember that the human brain has got certain advantages over the computer: it costs less and it can be made by unskilled labor.

Finally, one comment on this programming technique using the nomenclature of Alvin Weinberg: Somehow the patrons have got to get across to the scientists the fact that running a nation is a *mission-orientated* project. This aspect of, if you like, the programming of faculties, universities, and scientists by the representatives of the public has fallen very much in arrears. There is another side to it which I have come across in places where there has been too close political control of scientific investigations. I think scientists have got to get across to patrons the idea that there is an inner cohesion of science. You cannot take what to an administrator might seem the most tidy and efficient course in solving a scientific problem. There is an inner logic that the scientist himself has to follow. That is why understanding between scientist and administrator is so important; when it breaks down and one gets dictation from the nonscientist to the scientist, all sorts of things go wrong.

Science is difficult to make "efficient," and I am very glad that Frederick Seitz has stated that big science must not be allowed to drive out little science. For you never know when little science will become big. Harvey Brooks has given a dramatic example of this, and I remember another one. I met in Hawaii, in 1930, men working on earthquake tremors. They did not know it, but they were laying the foundation on which, if there ever is one, a nuclear arms control will be based. One cannot predict the future of any particular kind of experiment, however crazy it seems. I think that, if I have learned one lesson from these papers, it is this: we need to devise systems for better programming of those who are our patrons in supporting scientific institutions and universities; and we need to ensure better programming of scientists and faculty by those who have to think of the over-all social and economic needs of the country.

BIOGRAPHICAL NOTES

ON CONTRIBUTORS

Abelson, Philip H.

Dr. Abelson's career as physicist led from the University of California where he was awarded a PH.D. in physics in 1939 to the Department of Terrestrial Magnetism, Carnegie Institution of Washington. In 1941 he joined the Naval Research Laboratory to develop a method of separation of uranium isotopes. After service as senior physicist and principal physicist at the Naval Research Laboratory in Washington, D. C., he became civilian in charge, NRL Branch, Navy Yard, Philadelphia (1944–45). He returned to the Department of Terrestrial Magnetism, Carnegie Institution of Washington as chairman of the Biophysics Section in 1946. He advanced to his present position as director of the Geophysical Laboratory of the Carnegie Institution in 1953, and he became editor of *Science* in 1962. He has received several awards including the Navy Distinguished Civilian Service Medal and the Hillebrand Award of the Chemical Society of Washington for 1962. A native of Tacoma, Washington, he received the B.S. in chemistry and the M.S. in physics from Washington State College.

Ashby, Sir Eric

Sir Eric Ashby is Master of Clare College, Cambridge, England and was formerly president and vice-chancellor of the Queen's University, Belfast. He has spent most of his working life in teaching and research in plant physiology. During World War II he was successively chairman, Australian National Research Council; director, Commonwealth Scientific Liaison Bureau; counsellor and acting minister, Australian Legation, Moscow. Since his return to England he has served on bodies concerned with scientific and educational planning (Advisory Council on Scientific Policy, Council for Scientific and Industrial Research, University Grants Committee), and he has been continuously involved in higher education in tropical Africa. In 1962–63 he was President of the British Association for the Advancement of Science. He is a Fellow of the Royal Society of London and holds honorary degrees from many universities.

Brademas, John

Congressman Brademas was graduated *magna cum laude* from Harvard with a B.A. degree in 1949. He obtained the D.PHIL. degree from Oxford University in 1954 where he was a Rhodes Scholar from the state of Indiana. He served in the U.S. Navy from 1945 to 1946 and for a time was assistant professor of political science at St. Mary's College, Notre Dame, Indiana. His experience has included positions as assistant to Adlai Stevenson, assistant to Senator Pat McNamara of Michigan, and assistant to Representative Thomas Ashley of Ohio. He was elected to the 86th Congress from the Third District, Indiana, and reelected to the 87th, 88th, and 89th Congresses.

Brooks, Harvey

Dr. Brooks received his A.B. degree from Yale, did graduate study at Cambridge, England, and received the PH.D. from Harvard in 1940. Following World War II he was professor of engineering at Pennsylvania State College and engaged in research at the Ordnance Research Laboratory there. He later held positions of research associate and Associate Laboratory Head at the General Electric Knolls Atomic Power Laboratory. In 1950 he became professor of applied physics at Harvard and advanced to Dean in 1957. He holds several patents in the area of nuclear power. He has served on several governmental technical advisory committees including the President's Science Advisory Committee.

Crewe, Albert V.

Born and educated in England, Dr. Crewe became a naturalized citizen of the United States in 1961. He joined the physics staff of the University of Chicago in 1955 and advanced from research associate to full professor in 1963. He became Director of the Argonne National Laboratory in 1961. His special work includes particle accelerator development and nuclear physics research. He is a member of several professional societies and the recipient of several awards from civic groups in Chicago.

Graham, Beardsley

Mr. Graham became the president and first employee of Spindletop Research in December, 1961. He was previously manager of Satellite Research Planning and Commercial Satellite Systems Organization, Lockheed Missiles and Space Company. Earlier he was Assistant Director of Stanford Research Institute and head of the Institute's Mountain States Division and served as technical consultant to the Vice President for Research, Bendix Aviation Company. As a result of his pioneering work with satellite communications, Mr. Graham was named by President Kennedy as one of the thirteen original incorporators of the Communications Satellite Corporation and served as a member of its board. He is also a member of the U.S. Atomic Energy Commission's Advisory Committee on Isotope and Radiation Development and Research Professor of Electrical Engineering, University of Kentucky. He is a Fellow of the Institute of Electrical and Electronics Engineers, a senior member of the American Institute of Aeronautics and Astronautics, and a founder and director of the Solar Energy Society.

Harris, William

Dr. Harris was born in Indiana and received the B.S. and M.S. degrees from Purdue University and the SC.D. from the Massachusetts Institute of Technology. A metallurgist, he was head of the Aircraft Armor Section, Bureau of Aeronautics, Navy Department, during World War II and held the rank of Lieutenant Commander. From 1947 to 1951 he was head of the Ferrous Alloys Group, Naval Research Laboratory. He has served on several advisory boards of the National Academy of Science–National Research Council and from 1960 to 1962 was assistant executive secretary for planning of the Division of Engineering and Industrrial Research. He joined the Battelle Memorial Institute in 1954 and is now Assistant to the Vice-President and Director of the Washington Office.

Since 1962 he has been chairman of the Government Liaison Committee of the Engineers Joint Council.

Haworth, Leland J.

Prior to his appointment as director of the National Science Foundation in 1963, Dr. Haworth served as a member of the U.S. Atomic Energy Commission. In his earlier career he taught physics successively at the University of Wisconsin and the University of Illinois. During World War II he was on leave from the University of Illinois to work on defense projects at the MIT Radiation Laboratory. He later became assistant director and then director of the Brookhaven National Laboratory, and in 1960 he was named president of Associated Universities, Inc., while continuing as laboratory director. He was a member of the board of directors of the Oak Ridge Institute for Nuclear Studies from 1959 to 1961. He was born in Michigan and received the A.B. and A.M. degrees from Indiana University and the PH.D. in physics from the University of Wisconsin in 1931. He was awarded the Certificate of Merit from the President of the United States for his World War II research.

Hornig, Donald F.

Dr. Hornig was born in Milwaukee in 1920. He received his B.S. from Harvard in 1940 and his PH.D. from the same institution three years later. He became Special Assistant to the President for Science and Technology in January, 1964. He was simultaneously named by the President to be chairman of the Federal Council for Science and Technology. Coincidentally, the Senate confirmed Dr. Hornig as director of the Office of Science and Technology in the Executive Office of the President. He also serves as Chairman of the President's Science Advisory Committee. His early experience included service at Los Alamos Laboratory and Brown University. He was appointed chairman of the Department of Chemistry at Princeton University in 1958 and was the first incumbent of the Donner Chair of Science at Princeton. He was elected to the National Academy of Sciences in 1957 and in 1959 was appointed to the Space Science Board of the NAS. He served on the President's Science Advisory Committee during the Eisenhower and Kennedy administrations.

Keenan, Boyd R.

Professor and Head, Department of Political Science, Purdue University, Dr. Keenan has combined a career of teaching and university administration. He holds both the A.B. and M.A. degrees from the University of Kentucky and the PH.D. degree from the University of Illinois. Prior to assuming his present position, Dr. Keenan was associate director of the Committee on Institutional Cooperation, an organization formed in 1958 by the presidents of the "Big Ten" universities and the University of Chicago to stimulate academic cooperation across state and institutional lines. While associated with the latter organization, he developed an interest in the administration of science. After accepting the departmental headship at Purdue University in 1964, he planned and directed the symposium upon which this volume is based.

Roush, J. Edward

Congressman Roush was born in Oklahoma and educated in Indiana. He received the A.B. degree from Huntington College and the LL.B. degree from Indiana University. He served in World War II as an infantry officer and was awarded the Bronze Star. He was recalled to duty during the Korean War and served from 1950 to 1952. He practiced law in Huntington, Indiana, and was prosecuting attorney for four years before his election to the U.S. Congress in 1958. He represented the Fifth District of Indiana in the 86th through the 89th Congresses and is a member of the House Committee on Science and Astronautics and the Committee on Government Operations.

Seitz, Frederick

A native of California, Dr. Seitz received the A.B. degree in mathematics from Stanford University and the PH.D. in physics from Princeton. After teaching physics for two years at the University of Rochester, he became a research physicist at the General Electric Company from 1937 to 1939. He returned to teaching in 1939 and taught successively at the

University of Pennsylvania, the Carnegie Institute of Technology, and the University of Illinois. From 1957 to 1962 he was head of the Physics Department at Illinois. Since 1962 he has been president of the National Academy of Sciences and was just recently reelected to a six-year term. His major professional scientific interest has been in the theory of solids and nuclear physics. He is now a member of the President's Science Advisory Committee and a member of the Defense Science Board, Department of Defense.

Teller, Edward

A native of Hungary, Dr. Teller received his university education in Germany and was awarded the PH.D. degree from the University of Leipzig in 1930. He came to this country and was professor of physics at George Washington University from 1935 to 1941 when he became a citizen of the United States. His wartime assignments took him from Columbia University to the University of Chicago in 1952, and since then to the University of California. One of the nuclear physicists who developed the world's first atomic bomb, Dr. Teller continued to work on nuclear weapons after Hiroshima and the end of World War II. He made significant contributions to development of atomic weapons and to the design of the world's first hydrogen bomb. He was a member of the General Advisory Committee of the Atomic Energy Commission from 1956 to 1958 and helped to establish the nation's second nuclear weapons laboratory at Livermore. He served as director of the Livermore Laboratory from 1958 to 1960. He has returned to academic life as professor-at-large of physics, and his current research is concerned chiefly with the peaceful applications of nuclear energy.

Thompson, Kenneth W.

Dr. Thompson, vice-president of the Rockefeller Foundation, holds M.A. and PH.D. degrees from the University of Chicago and the LL.D. from the University of Notre Dame. He has served with the Rockefeller Foundation since 1953 in the area of international relations and social sciences. During World War II he was an officer in counterintelligence. He formerly taught political science at the University of Chicago and at Northwestern

University. He has presented endowed lectureships at Riverside Church in New York, at Duke University, and at Rice University. His many publications have been in both the area of international relations and in moral and political theory.

Triolo, James S.

A native Californian, Mr. Triolo received the A.B. and A.M. degrees from Stanford University. His early career was as a high school teacher in California and Hawaii and as a swimming coach in the Central American Olympics. He served with the U.S. Canal Zone Government just prior to World War II, and during the war he was Secretary of the American Embassy in Colombia. He has engaged in public relations and sales work in New York City. For nine years he was connected with the administration of Stanford University. In 1950 he became executive director of the Development Board of the University of Texas, and in 1963 he assumed his present position as vice president for development and public information of the Graduate Research Center of the Southwest.

Weinberg, Alvin M.

Now Director of the Oak Ridge National Laboratory, Dr. Weinberg came to Oak Ridge from the University of Chicago Metallurgical Laboratory in 1945 as a Section Chief in the Clinton Laboratories Physics Division. After serving as Director of the Division for ten months, he was appointed Research Director of the Laboratory in 1948 and continued in that capacity until his present appointment in 1955. Dr. Weinberg was responsible for the early conception of the pressurized water cycle for reactors now used in the nuclear navy and was also responsible for the early development of the Power Package Reactor. He was co-winner of the 1960 Atoms for Peace Award, granted in recognition of his role in the development of nuclear reactors. In June, 1960, Dr. Weinberg was one of five recipients of the U.S. Atomic Energy Commission's first E. O. Lawrence Memorial Award, which was presented in recognition of his contributions to nuclear reactor theory and for work in the design of production, research, and power reactors.